Table of Contents

About the Stories

Through biographies and realistic fiction, students will learn about people, events, and ideas that represent the grand diversity of the people of North America.

While providing reading practice, the 20 stories in *Read and Understand, Celebrating Diversity, Grades 3–4* present ideas and information that address diversity objectives in current standards outlined by the National Council for the Social Studies.

The stories in this book progress from third- to fifth-grade reading levels. When dealing with biographies and social studies content, certain specific vocabulary is necessary. For this reason, the readability of some of the stories in this book may be at a higher level than students can read independently.

How to Use the Stories

We suggest that you use the stories in this book for shared and guided reading experiences. Prior to reading, be sure to introduce any vocabulary that students may find difficult to decode or understand. A list of suggested words to teach is given on pages 3 and 4.

The Skills Pages

Each story is followed by four pages of activities covering specific reading skills:

- comprehension

- vocabulary

- making connections to students' own lives—comparison, evaluation, feelings

- making connections to the curriculum—mathematics, geography, written language, etc.

Vocabulary to Teach

The content of the stories in *Read and Understand, Celebrating Diversity, Grades 3–4* requires that specific vocabulary be used. This vocabulary is often at a higher level than might be expected for the grade level. We suggest, therefore, that you introduce these words before presenting the story. It is also advisable to read the story in advance to pinpoint additional words that your students may not know.

A Page from Diane's Diary 5
cinnamon, relieved, zucchini, doughnuts, wheelchair, special

Diary of a Biracial Child 11
supportive, weird, audition, annoying, impressed, elementary, character, judgments, considered, combination, heritage, ignore, jealous, compliment, common

Nick's Tourette Syndrome 19
injure, control, disorder, tics, repeated, movements, severe, unfortunately, medication, concentrate, unpleasant, guinea pig, impossible, depressed, information, suggested, curious, successful, accountant

My Name Is Gao Yang 26
Hmong, Laos, Southeast Asia, government, communist, Pathet Lao, soldiers, Vietnam, survive, Thailand, Mekong River, refugees, California, Fresno

Cesar Chavez, Dolores Huerta, and the United Farm Workers 33
Arizona, adobe, disappointment, grueling, labor, conditions, irrigation, migrants, graduated, Spanish, Stockton, suffering, volunteered, citizenship, union, association, La Causa, urged, convinced, huelga, courage, boycott

Benito's Grandpa 41
karate, academy, signaled, approaching, progress, duffel bag, sirens, disappearance, diagnosed, Alzheimer's, confused, dependent, mourned, witnessed, competitive

Martin Luther King, Jr. 48
Atlanta, Georgia, equal, allowed, succeed, college, Mohandas Gandhi, Britain, India, nonviolent protest, arrested, peaceful, minister, pastor, Coretta Scott, Baptist, Montgomery, Alabama, boycott, weapons, civil rights, organize, movement, equality, Lincoln Memorial

A Letter to My Family 56
finally, New York City, miserable, opportunities, Nicholai, Pittsburgh, Pennsylvania, language, disrespectful, equally, spirits, Oregon, festival, immigrated, Yugoslavia, business, pronounce

A New School 62
Maria, migrant, Colorado, distant, assured, familiar, ¿Qué pasa?, tetherball

A Day in the Life of an Amish Girl 68
Rosanna Fischer, faint, Hostetler's, whinnied, rhythm, community, applesauce, churned, crockery, Rachel, admire, snuggled

Meet Tamir Goodman 75
teenager, religion, Jewish, yarmulke, skullcap, observes, Sabbath, colleges, expected, comfortable, example, sportswriters, faith

The Cajuns 80
Acadia, Louisiana, Cajuns, descended, French, Canada, Mardi Gras, celebration, New Orleans, costumes, gumbo, Basile, fabulous, excitement, okra, plea, beckons

Mollee's Story 86
prosthesis, artificial limb, accepted, trudged, reactions, particular, cruel, conversation, concerns, treatment, disability, respond, situation, approached, tango, nervousness, confidence, inquired, absolutely, despised, Jenaya, casually, satisfied, guardedly optimistic, accepting, mature, decision

Hideo Nomo 93
Japanese, professional, dedication, Osaka, Japan, sumo wrestler, superb, honor, Shizuo, Kayoko, advanced, unagi, sakana, tutors, encouraged, Little League, Ikeshima, essay, talented, Olympics, Seoul, South Korea, respectably, announcers, tornado, retired, interpreter, communicate, language barrier, competes, National League

The Road to Recovery 100
Kalen, ordinary, carefree, extremely, automatic, therapist, weakening, fortunately, anxious, passion, determined, continued, disappointment, prepare, reduced, exercised, junior varsity, dedication, determination

Ben Nighthorse Campbell 107
Native American, United States Congress, Cheyenne, heritage, cruel, violent, affected, encouraged, comfortable, employers, discriminated, discrimination, community, alcoholic, tuberculosis, especially, judo, defend, appearance, accepted, popular, athletic, Korean War, San Jose, progress, championship, martial arts, Pan American Games, individual, ancestry, minorities

Kwanzaa 114
jambo, rafiki, Dr. Maulana Karenga, honoring, heritage, culture, African, importance, festivals, kinara, principles, unity, self-determination, collective, responsibility, cooperative economics, purpose, creativity

Jackie Robinson 119
Georgia, Pasadena, California, delivering, errands, stadium, University of California at Los Angeles, drafted, Kansas City Monarchs, Negro American League, major leagues, Branch Rickey, Brooklyn Dodgers, Montreal Royals, determination, deserved

Michelle Kwan 125
immigrants, China, achieve, gymnastics, comfortable, Olympic champion, Brian Boitano, determination, competition, senior, accepted, national competitions, successes, disappointments, experienced, flawlessly, Nagano, Japan, Tara Lipinski, athlete

Thurgood Marshall 131
punishment, Constitution of the United States, memorized, amendment, citizens, segregated, segregation, permitted, confused, Lincoln University, Pennsylvania, lawyer, Howard University, admired, professors, excellence, graduation, Baltimore, Maryland, National Association for the Advancement of Colored People, education, educated, improve, appreciate, Supreme Court, potential, achievements, justice, President John F. Kennedy, President Lyndon B. Johnson, appointed

A Page from Diane's Diary

Dear Diary,

    I love going to the grocery store. I like all the rows of pretty packages. I love how shiny and neat everything is.

    My job is to push the cart around the store. My mom and I both take items from the shelves. I put them in the cart. I like to arrange everything very carefully. I make sure that the soft things, like bread and tomatoes, are always on top!

    Today there were all kinds of things on our list. We needed chicken, milk, and peanut butter. In the produce department we chose celery, apples, and zucchini. I picked out Sweetie Pops cereal. Mom wanted Healthy Crunch. Then we got a box of doughnuts for a treat. Yum!

    Finally there was only one item left on our list. It was cinnamon. So my mom and I wheeled into the aisle where the spices are. I spotted the cinnamon. It was way up on the top shelf. I stretched on my tiptoes, but I couldn't reach it. A man was putting bags of sugar on a shelf nearby. I asked him to get the cinnamon down for me. He said he would be happy to help. Of course, I said, "Thank you." I put the little brown bottle in our cart.

    Then we headed to the check-out line. A lady with a little boy about six years old was ahead of us. He turned and stared at us.

    "Mommy, what's wrong with that lady?" He blurted it out in a loud voice. His mother turned red. She pulled on the boy's shirt.

    "Jimmy, come here. It isn't polite to stare."

    This happens to us all the time, so it was no big deal. My mom did what she always does. She just smiled and reached out her hand.

Celebrating Diversity • EMC 797

"It's okay. Hi, Jimmy! Would you like to see my wheelchair?"

Jimmy's mom looked relieved. Jimmy came right over. He was smiling, too, but he seemed kind of shy.

"You see, Jimmy, my legs don't work. I have to use a wheelchair to get around."

"Do you drive it on the street?" he asked.

"No," my mom said, laughing. "I have a special car for that. It lets me do all the driving with only my hands."

"Wow," said Jimmy. "That's cool."

"She even has a bike with hand pedals. We go bike riding all the time. In fact, Mom can do everything. . .except for one thing."

"What is it?" asked Jimmy.

"She can't reach things that are up high."

"Like cinnamon," said Mom, with a twinkle.

"Hey," said Jimmy, "maybe you could get a wheelchair with an elevator in the seat! Then you could reach higher than anybody!"

"What a good idea," said Mom. "Maybe some day you can invent one for me!" We all laughed. Then Jimmy and his mom said good-bye.

I pushed our cart up to the counter. I helped put our things in paper bags. I wanted to make sure that the doughnuts were on top so they wouldn't get squished.

As I said before, I love going to the grocery store.

Until tomorrow,
Diane

Questions about *A Page from Diane's Diary*

1. Why does Diane like to go to the grocery store? Give at least two reasons.

_____

_____

_____

2. What did Jimmy's mother do when Jimmy shouted, "What's wrong with that lady?" How did she feel? How do you know?

_____

_____

_____

3. What did Diane's mother do in response to Jimmy's question? How did she feel? How do you know?

_____

_____

_____

4. How do you think Diane feels about her mom?

_____

_____

_____

Name_____

A Page from Diane's Diary
Categories

Some of the foods that Diane and her mother bought are listed in the categories below. Think of several items to add to each category.

Meat	Dairy	Produce	Bakery
chicken	milk	celery	doughnuts
		apples	
		zucchini	

Synonyms

Synonyms are words that have about the same meaning. Draw a line from each word on the left to its synonym on the right.

store	bashful
loud	mashed
polite	small
squished	noisy
happy	mannerly
little	market
shy	cheerful

Name_____

A Page from Diane's Diary
How Do You Help?

Diane helps her mother do the grocery shopping. What chores do you help your family do?

_____

_____

_____

Write a paragraph describing your favorite chore. Explain what you do, how it helps your family, and why you like to do it.

_____

_____

_____

Draw a picture to illustrate your paragraph.

Name_____

A Page from Diane's Diary
Grocery Store Math

Solve each problem.

Work Space

1. Diane and her mom bought a chicken.
   It cost $0.79 per pound. It weighed 4 pounds.
   How much did the chicken cost?

   _____

2. The doughnuts Diane chose were on sale.
   The usual price was $2.49. The sale price
   was $1.89. How much did Diane save on
   the doughnuts?

   _____

3. The box of Sweetie Pops cost $2.29.
   The box of Healthy Crunch cost $3.17.
   How much did the two boxes of cereal
   cost in all?

   _____

4. Apples were priced at $0.25 each.
   Diane's mom told her to put $2.00
   worth of apples in a bag. How many
   apples did Diane get?

   _____

5. Zucchini was priced at $0.55 per pound.
   Diane's mom bought 2 pounds.
   How much did the zucchini cost?

   _____

Diary of a Biracial Child

October 13

Dear Diary,

I am so excited about the school play. I'm trying out for the lead. Sarah Jacobs is trying out too. All of my friends say that I'm a much better actress than she is. I think they're just being nice. I do feel good about my chances, though.

Mom and Dad are very supportive. They even sent me to theater camp last summer. I think they're the best parents in the whole world. They aren't like most parents. My mom is white and my dad is black. This isn't always easy. Sometimes when I'm shopping with my mom, people stare at us. It's weird. Do we look that different from other mothers and daughters?

I'll let you know tomorrow how the audition went.

Love,
Jamie

October 14

Dear Diary,

At the audition I got to read with Michael Anderson. Michael is trying out for the male lead role. I hope we both get lead parts. Sarah Jacobs read with Andrew Miller. She forgot most of her lines. It was really annoying the way she kept tossing her blond hair.

Mr. Davis seemed impressed by my audition. Three other teachers I've had were judges. They know I work hard and get straight A's. Mr. Davis said he would post a cast list by the end of the week. I don't think I can wait.

Love,
Jamie

Celebrating Diversity • EMC 797

October 15

Dear Diary,

I'm still waiting to see if I get the lead role in the school play. Our elementary school puts on a play every fall. I've always been in it, but I've never gotten the lead. I know I have a good shot at it. I did hear something today that's bothering me. Sarah Jacobs said that the characters in the play are white. She says I don't have a verygood chance at the lead because I'm not white. What's she talking about? I'm white, aren't I?

Love,
Jamie

October 16

Dear Diary,

I wrote to you after school that Sarah Jacobs said I wouldn't get the lead because I wasn't white. Well, I asked my parents about it at dinner. They both said that when they look at me they don't see a color. They just see their daughter. I don't see color when I look at people either.

I don't get why people make judgments about you because of the color of your skin. I guess I've always considered myself white and black. My parents say that I'm a perfect combination of both of them. I'm fair skinned like my mother. I even have freckles on my nose like her. And I'm tall and lean like my dad. I have his coarse brown hair and it's very curly. (This I hate!) My brother looks more like my dad. His skin is darker. He looks black.

Love,
Jamie

October 18
Dear Diary,

Sorry I didn't write yesterday, but I was too upset. I didn't get the lead in the play. Sarah Jacobs will be the star. She's done nothing but gloat about it for two whole days. Could she have been right about the reason I didn't get the part?

When I talked to my mom about not getting the part she wasn't much help. She said there would be other plays. Mom had told me to be happy with the part that I did get. She said if Mr. Davis didn't pick me because of my mixed heritage, it was his problem. How come it feels like my problem?

Love,
Jamie

October 20
Dear Diary,

I decided to talk to Mr. Davis today about why I didn't get the part. He told me it wasn't because of my color. In fact, what he said made me feel better. He said he picked me to play the main character's mother because it's a more interesting part that requires more of the actor. He said he had me in mind when he chose this play.

I did tell him what was bothering me. I told him about Sarah saying it was a white play. He said this wasn't true. In fact, he'd seen the same play in New York. The characters were played by people from around the world.

Love,
Jamie

October 21

Dear Diary,

We started play practice today. It was great. I love my character. She's very interesting. I think Mr. Davis was right. I am perfect for this part.

I'm working really hard to ignore Sarah. She just seems to get under my skin. Mom told me Sarah says things because she knows it bothers me. I can't help it. She's so perfect. She has blond hair, blue eyes, and perfect skin. I guess I'm jealous.

Love,
Jamie

October 22

Dear Diary,

Sarah actually gave me a compliment today. I couldn't believe it. She told me she was jealous of my hair! Can you believe it? I hate my hair and she's jealous of it! She said she always wanted dark curly hair. I told her I always wanted straight blond hair. Don't tell anyone, but I think I actually like Sarah. It turns out that we have many common interests. I'm actually going to her house tomorrow so we can practice our lines!

Love,
Jamie

Drawing Conclusions about *Diary of a Biracial Child*

Complete the statements below by writing conclusions.

1. Because Jamie didn't get the lead in the school play, she believed

_____

2. Jamie was a good student. Her teachers were judges for play tryouts, so she hoped

_____

3. Sometimes Jamie and her mother were stared at when they were out shopping. Jamie thought

_____

4. After Mr. Davis told Jamie why he gave her another part, Jamie realized

_____

5. Jamie and Sara ended up having many things in common, so Jamie believed that

_____

6. When Jamie couldn't wait until the cast list was posted, you conclude that Jamie

_____

Name_____

Diary of a Biracial Child
Synonyms

Write a **synonym** from the box for each word below from the story.

Word Box				
bothering	encouraging	amazed	opinions	brag
reject	difficulty	praise	needs	envious

1. supportive _____

2. annoying _____

3. impressed _____

4. judgments _____

5. gloat _____

6. ignore _____

7. compliment _____

8. problem _____

9. jealous _____

10. requires _____

Name_____

Diary of a Biracial Child
Starting a Diary

Keeping a diary is one way of recording information you don't want to forget.
Write a diary entry in the box below. Write about anything you'd like. Here are
some ideas if you need some help getting started.

- Has there ever been a time when you felt you were treated unfairly?
  Describe it.

- What's the funniest thing that's happened to you this year?

- What is your greatest fear?

- When you grow up, what would you like to do with your life?

_____
Date

Dear Diary,

_____

_____

_____

_____

_____

_____

_____

_____

_____

Name_____

Diary of a Biracial Child
Picture Perfect

Writing a diary or journal is one way to record important events in your life. Pictures and videos are other ways to keep memories alive.

But how could you keep track of information without words or technology? Art!

In the space below, draw something in your life right now that you want to remember. It could be a person, place, or thing.

Nick's Tourette Syndrome

Nick's desk fell over with a loud crash. Papers, pencils, and books went flying. His arms had been crossed in his lap. Suddenly they flew up, knocking the desk over. The room fell silent. Nobody made eye contact with him. A few children looked at the mess, but no one said a word. Nick was used to this. Slowly he picked up his desk. He hoped that there wouldn't be more tics before he got things cleaned up.

Nick has Tourette syndrome. When Nick was five years old, his parents knew something wasn't right. Sometimes he'd cough a lot when he wasn't sick. He'd laugh at the wrong times. His head would jerk to one side for a long time. Sometimes his shoulders would shrug until they ached. Many times he'd bump into walls and doors and injure himself. At first his parents got angry. They told him to stop. But Nick couldn't control himself.

For a year he went to doctor after doctor. The doctors just didn't know what was wrong. Then came the answer—Nick suffered from Tourette syndrome. TS is a lifelong disorder. It strikes boys more often than girls. A person with TS has tics. Tics are repeated body movements like blinking, jerking of the arms, legs, or head, or making noises.

Sometimes Nick could control the tics. But when he was angry or excited, the tics were more severe. Then he couldn't control them at all. The doctors used different medicines to try to control the tics. Each medicine had unpleasant side effects.

His parents were unhappy with the medication he'd been on recently. They'd decided to have Nick stop taking it. Nick was glad about this. The medication made him very tired. Most of the time he just slept through class. He was missing a lot of schoolwork. He couldn't concentrate and his grades were going down.

Unfortunately, he knew that he'd soon be given another medication. He felt like a guinea pig. The doctors were always trying out new treatments on him. So far none of them had worked. The tics always came back. They might be under control for a while, but they always came back.

Poor grades didn't bother Nick as much as something else. He wanted so badly to fit in, to have friends. So far, this had been impossible. Just when he made a new friend, his TS would kick in. He might clap his hands, shout loudly, or even spit. People looked at him as if he were a freak. Sometimes his classmates would point and laugh.

It was so unfair. He couldn't help the way he acted. He tried to control the TS, but this just made it worse. Nick didn't have anyone to talk to. He didn't have anyone to play with. Kids at school didn't want to have anything to do with him. Nick always felt alone and depressed.

His parents were very worried about Nick. Then they had an idea. They gave Nick's teacher information about Tourette syndrome. She suggested that the school nurse talk to the class. Nick was unsure about this. He was afraid it would just make things worse. Then he decided things couldn't get any worse than they already were.

After the school nurse showed a film about TS, there was time to talk. The kids were really curious about the disorder. They asked Nick many questions. Nick was glad to answer them. Nick was shocked when Jeff said that his dad had TS and he was a successful accountant. Nick could feel his classmates' fear begin to disappear. The door to understanding Nick's TS was opened.

That night at dinner, Nick's parents asked him what he thought about the day. Nick excitedly told them it had gone well. Just then the phone rang. It was for Nick—the phone was never for him! It was Jeff. He wanted Nick to come over to play after school the next day.

After he hung up, Nick couldn't quit smiling. Things were going to get better. He was sure of it.

Name_____

Questions about *Nick's Tourette Syndrome*

1. Describe what Tourette syndrome is like.

_____

_____

_____

2. Tell about two tics that Nick suffered from.

_____

_____

_____

3. Why does Nick think his classmates don't want to have anything to do with him?

_____

_____

_____

4. In the story, Nick said he could "feel his classmates' fear begin to disappear." What do you think this means?

_____

_____

5. Why did Nick think things were going to get better after Jeff's phone call?

_____

_____

Name_____

Nick's Tourette Syndrome
Vocabulary Scramble

Unscramble each vocabulary word. Then write the letter of its correct meaning. The first one has been done for you.

Word Box			
medication	control	curious	treatment
severe	depressed	concentrate	suggest

1. tioncdimea   _medication_   _b_

2. cenocetartn   _____   ____

3. veesre   _____   ____

4. tentramte   _____   ____

5. noclort   _____   ____

6. dedeserps   _____   ____

7. gsuegst   _____   ____

8. rucuiso   _____   ____

a. to focus

b. a substance used to treat an illness

c. sharp; violent

d. to hold steady; keep within bounds

e. nosy; interested

f. to offer an opinion or information

g. sad; gloomy

h. medical care

Nick's Tourette Syndrome
Walk in Someone Else's Shoes

1. Nick's differences kept him from being accepted by his classmates. Imagine that you are one of Nick's classmates. Why are the kids having trouble accepting him?

_____

_____

_____

2. What would you do to make Nick feel more like part of the class?

_____

_____

_____

3. Now imagine that you are Nick. How do you think it would feel to have Tourette syndrome?

_____

_____

_____

4. If you were Nick, what do you think you could do to make friends with your classmates?

_____

_____

_____

Name_____

Nick's Tourette Syndrome
Feeling Special

In the story, Nick didn't feel that he had any friends. He felt hopeful when Jeff, one of his classmates, called to invite him over. In the space below, make a list of ways to make someone feel special and part of the group. The first three have been done as examples for you.

1. call them on the telephone

2. ask them to play a game

3. sit by them at lunch

4. _____

5. _____

6. _____

7. _____

8. _____

9. _____

10. _____

11. _____

12. _____

13. _____

14. _____

15. _____

My name is Gao (Gou) Yang. I am an American. I am also Hmong. My family came here from Laos. Laos is a country in Southeast Asia. We had to leave because of a war. Some people in our country wanted our government to be communist. They were called the Pathet Lao. The Hmong people wanted to be free. We fought against the Pathet Lao. We also helped the American soldiers who were fighting in Vietnam. (Vietnam is the country next to Laos.)

The Pathet Lao won the war. They were very angry with the Hmong. It was a scary time. My parents had to hide in the jungle to survive. They did not have a home. They did not have enough to eat. They were always afraid.

Finally they decided to escape to Thailand. It would be very dangerous. They would have to swim across the Mekong River. They would go at night. If the Pathet Lao soldiers caught them, they would be killed.

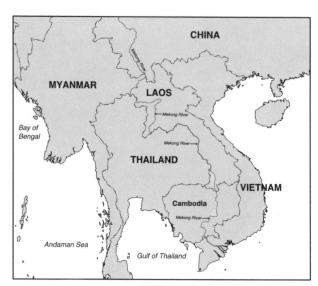

But my parents were very brave. They waited for a moonless night. They made their way to the river. In the inky darkness they slipped into the river. They swam as hard as they could. They used pieces of wood to help them float. It seemed as if they would never reach the other side. The sky was beginning to turn light as they dragged themselves onto Thailand's friendly shore.

In Thailand there were many Hmong people. They were living in camps for refugees. Refugees are people who need a safe place to stay. They are people who had to leave their homes because of danger.

My parents settled into a camp. Here, at least, they had food and shelter. They were happy at the camp. My mother says a wonderful thing happened there. I was born! But my parents did not want to stay in the camp forever. They were not sure what to do next. They could not go back to Laos.

At last they decided to try to go to the United States. My mother and father had brothers and sisters who were already living in California. My aunts, uncles, and cousins wanted us to come. They told my parents how wonderful life was in America.

My parents were full of feelings as they got on board the airplane. My mother carried me in her arms. My father carried a suitcase full of clothes. My mother has told me many times how she cried as the plane took off. She was sad to leave behind the only world she knew. She was happy because she hoped we would find a better life ahead.

California was a big change for my parents. They had never lived in a house with running water. My mother had always cooked meals over an open fire. Neither of my parents had driven a car or had a telephone. I love to hear them tell about how they turned the light switches on and off just for fun. Or how they ran hot water into the sink and laughed for joy. It was a very different world.

Not everything about it was fun and easy. It was hard to learn English. My mother said the sounds did not fit in her mouth. And there were many other things to get used to. There were new smells, new tastes, and even new weather. But my family was lucky. Our friends and relatives helped us. We quickly made new friends too.

My parents found jobs. At night they went to school to learn English. Our family grew. Two sisters were born. Slowly my parents began to feel that Fresno was really home.

For me, Fresno has always been home. Sometimes, when my father tells stories of the misty green mountains of Laos, I can almost believe that I have seen them. I hope someday I will be able to go and see my other homeland.

But for now, I am happy. My family is safe. We have a good home. We have a strong community. I speak English and Hmong. I study hard because I want to be a teacher. I want to help other refugee families who come to America looking for a new start.

Name_____

Questions about *My Name Is Gao Yang*

1. Why did Gao's family have to leave Laos?

_____

_____

2. What were some of the things that were different about their new home in America?

_____

_____

_____

3. Gao feels that he has two homelands. Explain.

_____

_____

_____

4. Gao's mother said that it was hard to learn English because **the sounds did not fit in her mouth.** What do you think she meant?

_____

_____

5. What does Gao want to be when he grows up? Why?

_____

_____

Name_____

My Name Is Gao Yang
Vocabulary

1. What are refugees?

_____

_____

2. Find four words in the story that describe feelings.

_____   _____

_____   _____

3. Find four words in the story that name the members of a family.

_____   _____

_____   _____

4. Draw a picture to illustrate the word given in each box.

jungle	river	mountains

Name_____

My Name Is Gao Yang
A Helping Hand

Moving to a new school, a new neighborhood, or a new country brings many challenges. Make a list of at least three ways you can help a newcomer to your classroom or neighborhood feel at home.

_____

_____

_____

_____

_____

Draw yourself doing one of the actions on your list.

Name_____

My Name Is Gao Yang
On the Map

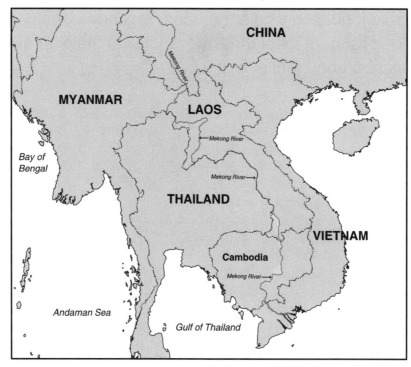

Use the map and the information in the story to answer these questions.

1. The Mekong River flows for more than 200 miles along the border
   between which two countries?

   _____   _____

2. Why are both of these countries important to Gao's family?

   _____

   _____

3. Name three other countries that border Laos.

   _____   _____

   _____

★★★ Cesar Chavez, Dolores Huerta, and the ★★★ United Farm Workers

When Cesar Chavez was a little boy, he lived with his parents and grandparents. They lived on a small farm in Arizona. All the family lived together in one little adobe house. There was no electricity. There was no running water. Times were very hard.

The family all worked at growing crops. They usually had enough food to eat. But it was hard to get a job. Nobody had much money to spend.

The family owed taxes on the farm. They needed money to pay the taxes. When they couldn't pay, the farm was taken away from the Chavez family. They would have to find another way to live.

Cesar's father decided to move his family to California. There he hoped to find work. But when they reached California, there was more disappointment. The only work to be had was farm labor. This was hard, grueling work. The pay was very little. The growers knew they did not have to pay much. There were thousands of people who wanted work. They would work for almost nothing. Cesar's father felt very sad. He knew there was no choice.

Cesar's mother and father went to work in the fields. They were paid only pennies per day. The children worked too. They spent long hours in the hot sun. They had little to eat or drink.

Living conditions for the farm workers were terrible. Families were crowded together in shacks or tents. They got water from the irrigation ditches. This water was filthy. It was unsafe to drink. People were often sick and hungry. Everyone had sore, aching muscles.

Cesar worked hard to help his parents. He went to school whenever he could. Going to school was difficult. Migrant workers had to move often. They had to go wherever the crops were waiting to be picked. Each move meant a new school. This made it hard to study. It was also hard to make friends. The teachers all spoke English. Sometimes they got angry when Cesar spoke Spanish. After Cesar graduated from the eighth grade, he left school for good. He had more years of schooling than most farm workers. Besides, he knew that his parents needed his help.

Dolores Huerta's early years were not much easier than Cesar's. She helped her mother run a hotel in Stockton, California. This little hotel took in migrant workers. The rooms were small and cheap. Often the men could not pay even the small price her mother charged. Instead they would bring bruised and damaged fruits and vegetables for payment. They could not be sold, so the growers allowed the men to take them. Dolores's mother would quietly accept whatever was offered. Sometimes this meant no payment at all.

Dolores saw how sad and hopeless the men were. They worked from daylight to dark. They worked day in and day out. Still they barely earned enough to survive on. They knew they could never get ahead. As they grew older, the hard work was more and more difficult. Dolores was just a young girl, but she knew that something was wrong. She knew she wanted to do something to help.

As the years went by, Cesar grew more and more unhappy. He was angry about the suffering of his family. He felt sad for all the other farm workers too. He wanted to help them. He just didn't know how. One night a man named Fred Ross came to speak to the farm workers. He understood their problems. He explained how they could take steps to improve their lives. Cesar was thrilled to be part of a group that was finally taking action. He volunteered a great deal of time. He helped farm workers fill out citizenship papers. He helped them register to vote. And he met another volunteer. Her name was Dolores Huerta.

Cesar and Dolores worked well together. They knew that their work was important, but Cesar and Dolores felt this work was going too slowly. They believed that more should be done. They felt that the farm workers should organize a union. Cesar and Dolores decided to take a big step. Together they formed the National Farm Workers Association.

The Association held many meetings. Cesar and Dolores talked to workers everywhere. They drove for miles to talk to workers in the fields. They urged them to join "La Causa," the cause. Cesar and Dolores worked without pay. They knew they had an important job. They were bringing hope to people who needed it badly. And their work paid off. The Association grew and grew.

Sometimes workers were afraid to join. They knew the growers would be angry. They might lose their jobs. How would they live? Dolores and Cesar convinced the workers that there was no other way. They had to join together. They had to demand better working conditions. It was the only way to make life better for themselves and their children.

In 1965 the Association voted to strike. They would not pick any grapes. Instead, they marched on the roads outside the farms. They carried signs with "Huelga!" written on them. (**Huelga** is the Spanish word for "strike.") They carried flags. The flags showed the outline of a black eagle. This eagle was the farm workers' symbol. It stood for strength and courage.

The growers did not like the flag. They did not like the marchers. They tried to frighten the marchers away. Sometimes they used violence against the marchers. They tried to hire other workers. But many of the new workers quickly joined La Causa.

By this time, the Association had changed its name. It was now called the United Farm Workers, or UFW. The UFW called for a boycott on buying grapes. People all over the country stopped buying grapes. They thought it was right to help the farm workers. The grape growers could not sell their grapes. They began to lose money. Finally, in 1970, they agreed to pay the farm workers more money. The strike was over.

Cesar Chavez spent the rest of his life working to help farm workers. He died in 1993. He will always be remembered as the founder of the UFW. He was a great champion of La Causa.

Dolores Huerta still works with the United Farm Workers. She is still trying to bring safe working conditions and fair pay to farm workers everywhere.

Name_____

Questions about *Cesar Chavez, Dolores Huerta, and the United Farm Workers*

1. Dolores and Cesar did not know each other when they were growing up, yet they shared some of the same feelings. Explain the feelings Dolores and Cesar shared.

_____

_____

_____

2. Why did Cesar leave school after the eighth grade? Give at least two reasons.

_____

_____

3. What were some of the problems faced by farm workers and their families?

_____

_____

_____

4. How are the lives of farm workers better because of Cesar Chavez and Dolores Huerta?

_____

_____

_____

Name_____

Cesar Chavez, Dolores Huerta, and the United Farm Workers
Vocabulary

A. Use the words in the box to complete the sentences below.

Word Box		
taxes	grueling	irrigation
crops	champion	migrant

1. The farmer's _____ need sunshine and water to grow.

2. Dan likes to cut firewood, even though it is a _____ task.

3. Martin Luther King, Jr., was a _____ of civil rights.

4. We pay _____ to the government.

5. The _____ family often dreamed of a permanent home.

6. The rancher brought water from the river to his fields by making

    _____ ditches.

B. The words on the left come from the Spanish language. Write the number of each word on the line in front of its English definition.

1. la causa   _____ strike

2. huelga   _____ sun-baked mud bricks

3. adobe   _____ the cause

Cesar Chavez, Dolores Huerta, and the United Farm Workers
Making Comparisons

Compare your life to the lives led by Cesar and Dolores when they were about your age.

How my life is different	How my life is similar

Name_____

Cesar Chavez, Dolores Huerta, and the United Farm Workers
Learning Spanish

uvas (**oo**-vas)	grapes
casa (**cah**-sah)	house
dinero (dee-**ner**-o)	money
abuelo (ah-**bway**-lo)	grandfather

Write the name of each picture in Spanish.

_____

_____

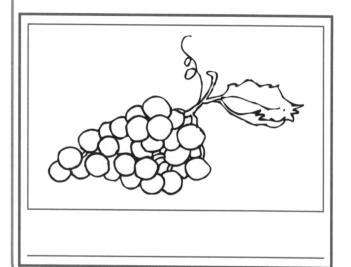

_____

_____

Benito's Grandpa

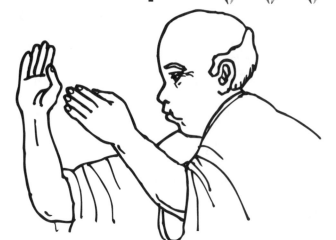

Benito and his grandpa both loved karate. It had been Grandpa who'd gotten him started. Grandpa was so excited when he'd caught Benito watching him practice.

"Benny, do you know what your old grandpa is doing?" Grandpa asked. He always called his grandson Benny, short for his real name, Benito.

"No, but it looks fun!" exclaimed Benito.

"I am practicing karate," Grandpa answered. "Would you like to join me?"

Thrilled, Benito grabbed Grandpa's hand. They moved to the center of the room. Grandpa patiently showed Benito several easy karate moves. Benito was just five years old then. That was when Grandpa had his own house. Now he lived with Benito and his mother. Grandpa had lived there since the day he'd forgotten to pick up Benito from karate practice.

On that day Benito waited on the steps of the karate academy for what seemed like hours. The chill in the air signaled that winter was quickly approaching. Little did he know that other changes were in store as well. Grandpa never missed Benito's karate practice. It was Grandpa who had planted the karate seed in his mind. Grandpa was always there to look after Benito's progress, much like a farmer tends to his crop.

"Where could he be?" Benito shouted to no one in particular. With that, he gathered up his duffel bag and headed for home. It wasn't as if he couldn't walk home alone. After all, he was nine years old. With his head down, he walked at a quick pace and headed for home.

He couldn't remember exactly what happened next. There were sirens and bright red lights. A small crowd was gathered in the front yard of his house. His mother was sitting on the steps. Her face was red and tears stained her cheeks. They found Grandpa hours later, but his disappearance started a painful family journey.

Grandpa was diagnosed with Alzheimer's disease. He did not forget Benito's lessons that day, his mother had explained. In fact, he had left the house not long after Benito that morning. The disease had caused him to become confused and he got lost. Benito thought the disease ruined everything. There were no more weekends at Grandpa's house. Grandpa couldn't teach him new karate moves anymore. Instead, Benito and his family started caring for Grandpa.

Caring for Grandpa day and night was difficult for Benito and his mother. Grandpa was dependent on them for everything. Sometimes Benito felt that he was caring for a small child, instead of his grandpa. Alzheimer's was like a snowball. It moved slowly downhill at first. Then with each day it gathered more snow and speed.

There were good days and bad days. On the bad days Grandpa wouldn't get out of bed. These were the days he didn't know who Benito was. Sometimes he'd know Benito's mother, but he remembered her as a child. Benito mourned for the way things used to be.

Once in a while, Benito would see flickers of light. One afternoon Benito walked into the living room and caught Grandpa looking at karate pictures. Outside, the wind howled. The falling snow blocked out the sun just as Alzheimer's blocked out his grandpa's memory.

"Benny, I remember the day you won this trophy," Grandpa said.

Surprised, Benny answered, "You do?"

"Of course I do. That was the first time I really witnessed your competitive edge. You reminded me of myself that day. I was so proud of you."

With his last words, Benito was choking back tears. "Grandpa, I'm so glad that you shared your love of karate with me," he said softly as they hugged.

"Me too, Benny, me too," Grandpa said as he rubbed Benito's back.

"Grandpa, I want things to be the way they were." He was sobbing now. Grandpa didn't say anything. He just squeezed Benito tighter. Benito decided his love for Grandpa could survive the Alzheimer's.

Name_____

Questions about *Benito's Grandpa*

1. The story said that Grandpa's disappearance started **a painful family journey.** What do you think that means?

_____

_____

_____

2. How was the relationship between Benito and Grandpa different after the diagnosis of Alzheimer's disease?

_____

_____

_____

3. Number these events from the story in the order in which they happened.

_____ Benito's grandpa was diagnosed with Alzheimer's.

_____ Grandpa taught Benito karate.

_____ Benito walked home from karate because Grandpa never showed up.

_____ Grandpa moved in with Benito and his mother.

_____ Mother was crying on the front steps of the house.

_____ Benito was surprised that Grandpa remembered when he won the trophy.

Name_____

Benito's Grandpa
Word Meaning

Write the number of each word on the line in front of its meaning.

1. patiently

2. academy

3. dependent

4. flickers

5. diagnosed

_____ needing help

_____ examined to identify a disease

_____ without complaint; willingly

_____ school

_____ short bursts of light

Similes

In the story *Benito's Grandpa* there are several similes. A **simile** compares one thing to another using the words **like** or **as**.

Her heart was beating **like** a speeding train.

Choose the word or words that correctly complete each sentence. Then find the simile in the story and write it on the lines.

1. Grandpa was compared to a

○ fireman   ○ farmer   ○ bus driver

_____

2. Alzheimer's was compared to a

○ speeding train   ○ black cloud   ○ snowball

_____

Name_____

Benito's Grandpa
A Letter to Someone Special

Benny and his grandpa both loved karate. What special activity do you share with someone in your family?

Write a letter to someone who is important to you. Tell the person what she or he means to you. Give examples of the interests or activities you share.

_____
Date

_____,

_____

_____

_____

_____

_____

_____

_____

_____

_____

_____,

_____

 Celebrating Diversity • EMC 797

Name_____

Benito's Grandpa
The Human Brain

The human brain weighs around three pounds. It is our body's master control. Like a computer, the brain stores information. When someone suffers from Alzheimer's disease, something goes wrong with the person's brain.

Study the diagram below to learn more about the brain.

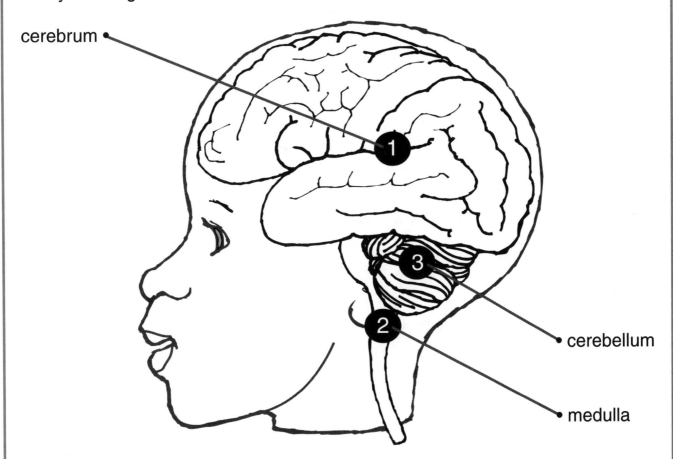

cerebrum

1

3

2

cerebellum

medulla

1. The **cerebrum** is the large rounded structure of the brain. It occupies most of the skull. Color the cerebrum gray.

2. The **medulla** is a part of the brain stem. It has nerve centers that control breathing, heartbeat, and other important body functions. Color the medulla blue.

3. The **cerebellum** is the part of the brain that controls posture, balance, and coordination of movement. Color the cerebellum red.

 # Martin Luther King, Jr.

Martin Luther King, Jr., was born on a cold winter day. The place was Atlanta, Georgia. The date was January 15, 1929. Martin's parents loved their children very much. They made a happy home for Martin and his sister and brother.

Things were not always easy for the King family. In those days, southern states had some bad laws called Jim Crow laws. Black people didn't have equal rights. This meant that black children could not go to school with white children. Black people had to sit in the back of the buses. They were not allowed in many shops and restaurants. Sometimes black people were hurt, or even killed, just because of their skin color.

Martin's parents taught him to believe in himself. They told him that he could succeed. But he knew that he would have to work extra hard to prove himself. He wanted to be a good person and make his mark in the world. He went to church every week and studied hard at school. Martin finished high school at 15 and was ready to go to college.

Martin liked college. He loved to read and learn about new ideas. One day he learned about a man who would change his life. This man's name was Mohandas Gandhi. Gandhi lived in India when Britain ruled that country. Gandhi wanted his people to be free. But he did not believe in fighting. Instead, Gandhi believed in nonviolent protest. He led his people on marches. He had his followers sit quietly in the middle of roads to block traffic. Sometimes they were arrested or beaten. Even then, they would not fight back. Gandhi was sure that his peaceful protests would work. After many years, India was free.

Martin thought Gandhi's ideas were very important. He thought they could be used to win equal rights for black people. He wanted to help his people gain true freedom. Martin thought that the best way to help was to become a minister. So he studied for many years. At last, he finished his schooling.

In 1953 Martin got married to Coretta Scott. Together, they decided that they should live in the South. Martin found a job as pastor of a Baptist church in Montgomery, Alabama. Martin and Coretta believed that they were needed in the South. They believed they could help make changes there. They settled into their new life. They began to make plans for a family of their own.

Everything went fine for about a year. Then something happened. It seemed like a small event, but it had a big impact on Martin. And it would forever change the nation.

On December 1, 1954, a black woman named Rosa Parks got on a city bus. She took a seat just behind the "whites only" section. The bus stopped to pick up more passengers. The driver asked Rosa to give up her seat. He wanted Rosa to stand up so that a white passenger could sit down.

Rosa refused. Her feet hurt and she was tired. The bus driver stopped the bus. He called the police. Rosa Parks was arrested and taken to jail.

Many people were angry. They planned a boycott of the city buses for the next Monday. That meant they would ask all the black people in Montgomery not to ride the buses. The buses would lose money. Martin urged the people at his church to join the boycott. It would be very difficult. They would have to carpool, take taxis, or walk to work. Some people had to walk several miles each way. But they did not care. They were tired of being treated badly.

The buses rolled empty on that Monday. The buses stayed empty for many days to come. Martin became a leader in the bus boycott. This took a lot of courage. Many whites were angry about the boycott. They did not want things to change. They did not care about making things better for black people.

One evening a bomb was thrown into Martin's house. Luckily his family was not hurt. But it was very frightening. News of the attack spread through the city. Martin's followers gathered at the King household. Police came too. The crowd was very tense.

Martin stepped out on the front porch. He spoke calmly. He told them to let go of their hatred. He said, "Violence must be met with nonviolence and hate must be met with love." The people calmed down. They went home to think about Martin's words.

Martin continued to work for civil rights for all people. He helped organize a movement that spread all across the land. Black and white people who believed in equality came together. They rode buses all around the South. They were called Freedom Riders. They would stop at places that were just for whites. Black Freedom Riders would use "whites only" bathrooms. White Freedom Riders would drink from "colored" water fountains. Sometimes they were beaten. Sometimes they were arrested and put in jail. It was difficult not to fight back. But they believed in Martin. They believed in their cause. Whatever happened, they would not give up.

Another kind of protest was the "sit-in." Black people would go to a "whites only" lunch counter. They would sit down. They would not be served, but they would not leave. Day after day, they would return to "sit in." Martin joined sit-ins and also led marches. He gathered thousands of followers and they would march through cities, singing about freedom:

> We shall overcome, we shall overcome
>
> We shall overcome, some day.
>
> Oh, deep in my heart
>
> I do believe
>
> That we shall overcome some day.

By 1963, sit-ins, marches, and boycotts were happening all over the South. On August 28, Martin led the famous March on Washington, D.C. Two hundred thousand people marched with him. They were black and white, rich and poor, old and young. They all shared a vision of a better America. They shared a dream. And as the crowd gathered by the Lincoln Memorial, Martin spoke about that dream.

"I have a dream," he said, "that my four little children will one day live in a nation where they will not be judged by the color of their skin but by the content of their character."

Martin Luther King, Jr., was killed just five years after he spoke these words. But his dream did not die. It lives on in the hearts of people who care about fairness. It lives on in the efforts of those who work for equal rights for all. It lives when we honor this great American.

Name_____

Questions about *Martin Luther King, Jr.*

1. What were the Jim Crow laws?

_____

_____

_____

2. Why was Gandhi so important to Martin?

_____

_____

_____

3. What did Rosa Parks do? How did her action affect Martin?

_____

_____

_____

4. Why did Martin tell his followers not to fight?

_____

_____

_____

5. Why do we remember Martin Luther King, Jr., today?

_____

_____

Name_____

Martin Luther King, Jr.
Vocabulary

A. Choose the correct answer.

1. In this story, the word **protest** means to
   ○ take an action against something you believe is wrong
   ○ study
   ○ look at something carefully

2. The words **minister** and **pastor** both appear in the story. They mean about the same thing. Where would a minister or a pastor work?
   ○ at a bank   ○ at a church   ○ at a factory

3. The people in Montgomery decided to **boycott** the buses. What does **boycott** mean?
   ○ to paint   ○ to break   ○ to not use

4. The word **vision** is used in this story to mean
   ○ eyesight   ○ idea   ○ explosion

5. Martin Luther King, Jr., believed in **nonviolence**. He did not want people to
   ○ fight   ○ sing   ○ sleep

B. Use these words to complete the sentences.

arrested   succeed   nation

1. People who work hard usually _____.

2. If you break the law, you might be _____.

3. Our fifty states make up one _____.

Name_____

Martin Luther King, Jr.
A Nonviolent Solution

Martin Luther King, Jr., told his followers that "hate must be met with love."

Think About It

Remember a time when you were very angry.
What were you angry about?
What did you do about it? Did you solve your problem nonviolently?

Write About It

What are some ways that you can use Martin's methods of nonviolence in your own life?

_____

_____

_____

_____

_____

_____

_____

_____

_____

_____

_____

Name_____

Martin Luther King, Jr.
Following in Gandhi's Footsteps

NJ Taylor

Mohandas Gandhi led the people of India to freedom. He is also known as Mahatma Gandhi. Mahatma is a special title of respect. It means "great soul."

Gandhi believed that people of all religions and races could live together in peace. He believed that people could solve problems without using violence.

Gandhi was a very small man, but he had great courage. He led marches and sit-ins. He was often put in jail, but he never gave up. It took more than thirty years of protest, but finally India was free.

It is easy to see why Gandhi is called "the father of India."

Use the clues below to write a synonym for the following words from the information about Gandhi.

1. **freedom:** 7 letters, starts with **l** _____

2. **courage:** 7 letters, starts with **b** _____

3. **jail:** 6 letters, has a short **i** _____

4. **father:** spelled the same in each direction _____

5. **violence:** base word rhymes with **kite** _____

 # A Letter to My Family

Dear Annie,

    I finally arrived in New York City on March 13, 1917. The ride over on the ship was long and miserable. I am happy to have finally arrived. I was seasick much of the trip. It was hard to leave my home of so many years and begin an adventure in a new land. I miss my family, but I'm excited about the new opportunities that await me.

    In New York I met a man named Nicholai who has been working for the steel mills in Pittsburgh, Pennsylvania. He offered me a job that pays two dollars a week. It took most of my money to buy a train ticket to get here.

    The work is difficult and the days are long. I am trying hard to learn the English language. The sounds of our language are hard for English speakers to say too. The foreman of my crew started calling me "Mike" because he could not pronounce my name. This name makes me feel more American.

    Many young Americans work with me. Some are very helpful, but others are so disrespectful. One fellow calls me names and laughs at the way I speak. He treats me as if I am not a man. I thought America was the country where everyone was treated equally. I will keep my spirits high. I plan to move west as soon as I have saved enough money. I hope to move to the lumber camps in Oregon by September.

Many Irish people who live here now celebrated St. Patrick's Day on March 17. There was lots of good food, fireworks, games, and singing. Never have I seen such a festival! It went on long into the night.

I think the Irish are treated worse than any other group that has immigrated to America. They are forced to take the lowest paying jobs. It takes hard work to make it in America. The Irish have shown me it can be done.

It has been only three month's time since I left Yugoslavia. I will save as much as possible so that you and Joseph can join me. One day we will have our own business and a nice house in which to raise our family.

In the next years many more people will be coming to America. I am thankful that I am here now. I know the promise of the United States will come true for us.

Your loving husband,
Mike

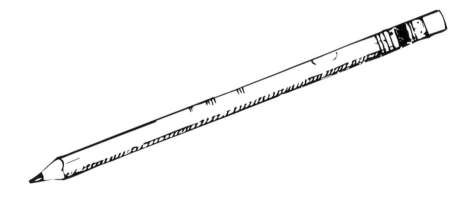

 Celebrating Diversity • EMC 797

Name_____

Questions about *A Letter to My Family*

1. Who wrote this letter to Annie? In what year was this letter written?

   _____

2. How did Mike describe his voyage to America?

   _____

   _____

3. Why do you suppose Mike was coming to America?

   _____

   _____

4. What country did Mike come from?

   _____

5. What were some of the difficulties Mike experienced during his first days in America?

   _____

   _____

6. What is Mike's hope for the future?

   _____

   _____

   _____

Name_____

A Letter to My Family
Vocabulary

A. Write the number of each word on the line in front of its definition.

1. fellow   _____ to come into a new country

2. disrespectful   _____ a resident of a city or town

3. miserable   _____ impolite; rude

4. festival   _____ nauseated; dizzy feeling

5. immigrate   _____ a man or boy

6. adventure   _____ extremely unhappy

7. seasick   _____ holiday or celebration

8. citizen   _____ exciting activity

B. Illustrate two of the words listed above. Label your drawings.

_____   _____

Name_____

Dear Annie,

A Letter to My Family
Tell It in Order

Number these events in the order in which they were mentioned in the letter.

_____ One day we will have our own business and a nice house in which to raise our family.

_____ Many Irish men and women who immigrated to this country before me celebrate St. Patrick's Day.

_____ I met a man named Nicholai who offered me a job in Pittsburgh, Pennsylvania.

_____ Annie, I arrived in New York City on March 13, 1917.

_____ I am working hard to learn the English language.

_____ The ride over on the ship was long and miserable, and I am happy to have finally arrived.

_____ I hope to move to the lumber camps in Oregon by September.

_____ It takes hard work to make it in America. The Irish have shown me it can be done.

Name_____

A Letter to My Family
Welcome to a New Land

The Statue of Liberty was one of the first landmarks immigrants saw as they entered New York Harbor. It was given to the United States in 1886 by France to symbolize freedom and opportunity in the New World.

Imagine you are traveling to a new land. What kind of landmark would you like to see? Illustrate your idea in the box below. Then explain what your landmark would symbolize.

Maria and her family had moved to the United States two years earlier. They had traveled around working on different farms. (People who do this are called migrant workers.) Now the family was living in Colorado. They planned to make this their home. Her dad and mom had picked potatoes in the state many times before. They liked the beautiful fields and distant view of the mountains. Maria liked it here too, but she was worried about going to a new school.

"I'm afraid to go to school," Maria told her mother. "What if the other kids laugh because I don't speak English?"

"You'll be just fine," her mother assured her. "You'll meet lots of new friends. It will be fun." But Maria still didn't feel any better.

On the first day of school, Maria's mother walked her to school. She introduced Maria to her new teacher. When the bell rang, Mother went home. Maria felt scared and lonely. The other children already knew each other. They were laughing and playing games. Maria was too shy to talk to anyone. "When will this day end?" she thought.

At lunchtime Maria sat by herself. At recess she watched the other kids having a great time. She wished she were still traveling from place to place where things were familiar. Suddenly Maria heard words she knew, "¿Qué pasa?"

Turning around fast, Maria saw one of her classmates. The girl was smiling and holding out her hand. "What's happening? I'm Anna. Would you like to play tetherball with me?"

Maria smiled and the two started toward the tetherball poles. After that, the rest of the day sped by.

Maria's mom was waiting for her when school was over. "How was your day?" she asked.

Maria smiled and said, "I think I'll try it again tomorrow." Then she gave her mom a big hug. They walked home together, both feeling happy about their new home.

Name_____

Questions about *A New School*

1. What was Maria worried about? Why?

_____

_____

_____

2. Maria's feelings changed from the beginning of the story to the end of the story. Choose the two words that best describe this change.

   ○ **frightened** to **sad**   ○ **happy** to **afraid**   ○ **nervous** to **relaxed**

3. Why had Maria's family traveled so much?

_____

_____

4. Where do you think Maria and her family lived before they came to the

   United States? _____

   Explain your answer.

_____

_____

5. Tell how you felt on the first day of school this year.

_____

_____

Name_____

A New School
Multiple Meanings

Read the two meanings for each word. Then read the two sentences. Write the letter of the correct meaning on each line.

1. **traveled**
   a. went from place to place   **b.** was transmitted

   _____ Maria and her family **traveled** around looking for work.

   _____ The radio signal **traveled** through the air.

2. **picking**
   a. nagging, teasing   **b.** gathering with the fingers

   _____ Her mom and dad had worked in the fields **picking** potatoes.

   _____ "Stop **picking** on your little sister," scolded Dad.

3. **shy**
   a. had less than a certain amount   **b.** uneasy around people

   _____ Maria felt too **shy** to talk to anyone.

   _____ She was $5.00 **shy** of being able to buy the bicycle.

4. **ring**
   a. a clear, piercing sound   **b.** a band worn on a finger

   _____ She lost her gold **ring** at the movies.

   _____ Maria listened for the school bell to **ring**.

5. **familiar**
   a. well known   **b.** had knowledge of

   _____ The lawyer was **familiar** with the facts of the case.

   _____ Suddenly Maria heard something **familiar**.

6. **settle**
   a. make a home   **b.** sink to the bottom

   _____ Maria's family planned to **settle** in Colorado.

   _____ The mud will **settle** on the bottom of the pond.

Name_____

A New School
Meet Maria

You have been chosen to write an article for your school newspaper about the new student at your school—Maria. Use the information from the story to summarize everything you know about Maria. Write your article in the box below.

MEET MARIA

CLASSROOM GAZETTE • VOL. 1   SEPTEMBER 11, 2000

Name_____

A New School
Friend Wanted

Think about the characteristics that make a good friend. Create a "Wanted" poster advertising for this new friend. Fill in the blanks below. Then draw a picture of your new friend in the box provided.

WANTED!
A SPECIAL FRIEND

WANTED FOR:

SPECIAL QUALITIES:

REWARD:

Draw here

     Celebrating Diversity • EMC 797

Rosanna Fischer woke up early. The light through her window was gray and faint. She heard the roosters crowing in the barnyard. She sniffed the air. She could smell potatoes frying and the scent of fresh bread. She smiled as she stretched beneath the pile of soft quilts. She was thinking of a warm slice of bread, spread thick with spicy apple butter.

Rosanna slipped out of bed. She carefully straightened the sheets. She plumped up her pillow. She smoothed the quilts. She worked quietly and quickly. The task was easy for her. She had learned to make her bed when she was very small.

A few simple dresses hung on a row of pegs. Rosanna chose the blue one. It had long sleeves and came down to her ankles. Over the dress, Rosanna put on a clean white apron. She pulled on her sturdy black boots and laced them up. Then Rosanna brushed her long hair, parting it down the middle. She rolled her hair neatly back from her face. Finally, she pulled a starched white cap over her hair and tied it under her chin. Rosanna glanced around her room to make sure everything was in order. Then she skipped down the stairs to breakfast.

After the morning meal, Rosanna helped her mother tidy the kitchen. Her father and brothers went out to the barn. The boys hitched the horse to the buggy while their father gathered the tools they would need for the Hostetlers' barn raising. The sun was just coming up as the family climbed into the buggy. Rosanna settled back, enjoying the rhythm and sway as the horse trotted down the road.

A half hour later they wheeled into the lane leading to the Hostetler home. The farm was buzzing with activity. Men and boys were working away, their voices and hammers ringing in the morning air. Chickens pecked in the yard, and horses grazed and whinnied in the pasture.

Rosanna followed her mother into the kitchen. There she found her best friend, Rachel Hostetler. The girls took a bucket of potatoes to an out-of-the-way corner of the kitchen and sat together. They didn't mind peeling potatoes. In fact, it would give them time to chat and giggle. Like all other Amish children, Rosanna and Rachel were expected to work. Even very small children could help in some way. All members of the family—and the community—worked together.

The morning went by quickly. The women made stewed chicken, homemade bread, biscuits, green beans, corn pudding, and applesauce. There were all kinds of pickles and jams and jellies too. Rounds of freshly churned butter gleamed on crockery plates. A dozen different pies cooled on the counters. Rosanna and Rachel cut each pie into neat wedges.

At noon the men took a break from their work. Everyone gathered together at long tables that had been set up outdoors. As always, the meal began with a prayer. The fresh air and hard work made everyone hungry. They ate happily. It was fun to eat good food with good friends.

The afternoon was just as busy as the morning had been. The men put the roof on the barn. The women washed the mountain of dishes. Then they sat together with their sewing. Rachel and Rosanna sewed too. Both girls were working on their very first quilts. They talked quietly as they stitched together the small pieces of pretty cloth.

As the late afternoon shadows fell across the farm, the men sent up a cheer. The barn was finished. Everyone trooped inside to admire the sturdy walls and strong beams. They brought chairs and benches for seats. All of the young people stood together in the center of the barn. Many older folks joined them. They marched and clapped their way through games such as Skip to My Lou and Bingo.

Rosanna and Rachel hardly sat down for a moment. It seemed the fun would last all night. But the long day of work had made everyone tired. At last the families began to say their good-byes. Tomorrow would be another day filled with work and family activities.

Rosanna snuggled into a pile of quilts in the back seat of the buggy between her brothers. Her father flicked the reins on the horse's back. Rosanna drifted off to sleep, lulled by the gentle sway of the buggy and the warm safety of her Amish world.

Name_____

A Day in the Life of an Amish Girl
Sequencing

A. Some of the events of Rosanna's day are listed below. Number them in the order in which they took place.

_____ Rosanna and her friend peeled potatoes.

_____ Rosanna got dressed.

_____ Rosanna made her bed.

_____ Rosanna arrived at the Hostetler farm.

_____ Rosanna heard roosters crowing.

_____ Everyone played games in the barn.

_____ Rosanna and Rachel worked on their quilts.

_____ The two girls cut the pies.

B. Write in order five events that happened to you today.

1. _____

2. _____

3. _____

4. _____

5. _____

Name_____

A Day in the Life of an Amish Girl
Vocabulary

Use the words in the box to complete these sentences.

1. The horses _____ loudly at each other.

2. We cleaned the house so it would be _____ when Grandmother arrived.

3. The cows _____ happily in the grassy meadow.

4. In the distance we heard the _____ sound of horses' hooves.

5. Donna pulled back on the _____ to make her pony stop.

6. When we visited New York City, we took a ride around Central Park in a

   _____ pulled by a horse.

7. Heavy dishes made from clay are called _____.

8. Before eating dinner, the family said a _____ together.

Word Box			
buggy	crockery	whinnied	faint
reins	grazed	tidy	prayer

Name_____

A Day in the Life of an Amish Girl
People Who Help

In this story you learned that members of the Amish community all work together to help each other.

Think about your own community. Name some of the people who help in your community. Tell how each of these people help.

Helper: _____

What he or she does to help: _____

_____

Helper: _____

What he or she does to help: _____

_____

Helper: _____

What he or she does to help: _____

_____

Think of something you and your family could do to help make your community better. Write about your idea.

_____

_____

_____

_____

Name_____

A Day in the Life of an Amish Girl
Quilting Shapes

A **quilt** is a bedcover made by sewing together small pieces of fabric into interesting patterns. Answer the questions about the quilt below.

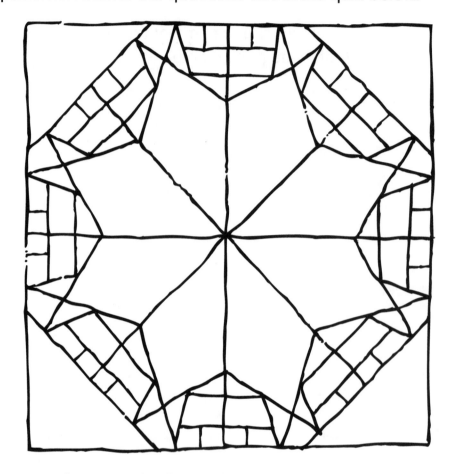

1. There are several geometric shapes in this quilt. Count the triangles and diamonds.

    triangles _____   diamonds _____

2. Color the quilt pattern.

3. Each quilt pattern has a name. What do you think would be a good name for this quilt pattern?

_____

Morning Gazette

MEET TAMIR GOODMAN

Tamir Goodman is a teenager. He is tall and skinny. He has red hair. And he loves to play basketball. In fact, he is very, very good at basketball. Magazines and newspapers have written stories about him. Thousands of people have come to watch him play. After high school, he plans to play basketball at college.

Lots of boys love to play basketball. What makes Tamir different from the others? Tamir puts his religion first. Tamir is Jewish. His religion gives him many rules for living. Jewish studies are part of each school day. He has times for prayer. He wears a yarmulke, or small skullcap, on his head.

Tamir observes the Sabbath. The Sabbath takes place from Friday at sundown until Saturday at sundown. This is a special time in the Jewish week. It is set aside as a holy day. Many activities are not allowed on the Sabbath. One of these is playing basketball.

Tamir knows that some colleges do not want him to be on their team. Many basketball games are played on Saturdays. He would be expected to play. Tamir believes that it is more important for him to be a good person than to be a good basketball player. For him this means following the rules of his religion.

Once during a basketball game, Tamir's yarmulke fell off his head. He stopped and pinned it back on in front of the whole crowd. He is comfortable with his religion. He is proud to be Jewish. He has helped other people be proud too. Other Jews have told him that they now wear yarmulkes because of his example.

Some sportswriters have given Tamir a nickname. They call him the "Jewish Jordan." Tamir thinks this is silly. He does not understand why people are paying so much attention to him. He just thinks of himself as a Jewish kid and a basketball player—in that order. For Tamir Goodman, faith will always come first.

Meet Tamir Goodman
True or False?

Write a **T** in front of each statement that is true. Write an **F** in front of each statement that is false.

_____ Tamir Goodman likes to play basketball.

_____ He is nine years old.

_____ Monday is the day of the Jewish Sabbath.

_____ Tamir thinks religion is more important than basketball.

_____ Tamir plans to go to college.

_____ Very few people have seen Tamir play basketball.

_____ Many college basketball games are played on Saturdays.

A Matter of Importance

Tamir Goodman's religion is more important to him than basketball. List four things that are important to you, beginning with the most important.

1. _____

2. _____

3. _____

4. _____

Name_____

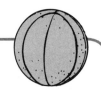

Meet Tamir Goodman
Vocabulary

A. Complete each sentence using one of the words in the box.

Word Box			
yarmulke	Sabbath	religion	activities

1. My favorite _____ are reading, playing tennis, and singing.

2. The _____ is a special holy day.

3. Dennis wears a _____ on his head.

4. People who follow the Christian _____ often go to church on Sunday.

B. Draw a picture to illustrate each of the following words:

crowd	basketball player

Name_____

Meet Tamir Goodman
In the News

A. What is the nickname magazine reporters gave to Tamir Goodman?

_____

B. Pretend that a magazine reporter is going to write a story about you. She wants to give you a nickname. What nickname would you choose? Explain your answer.

_____

_____

_____

_____

_____

Draw a picture of yourself that you'd like to see included in the newspaper article.

Name_____

Meet Tamir Goodman
The Story of Basketball

Basketball was invented more than 100 years ago. The year was 1891. A teacher named James Naismith wanted to make up a game that his students could play indoors. He wanted a game that could be played in the winter months.

Mr. Naismith made up 13 rules for the game. He asked the janitor at his school to hang a box at each end of the gymnasium. The boxes would be used as goals. The janitor could not find any boxes. He found some baskets instead. Mr. Naismith said that baskets would be fine.

Mr. Naismith taught his students how to play the new game. The students had fun playing the game. There was only one problem. Whenever a player scored a basket, someone had to climb up a ladder to get the ball. They soon cut a hole in the bottom of the basket. Then someone thought of using a rim with a net.

Changes have been made to the basket, the ball, and the rules over the years. But one thing remains the same. Basketball is still fun to play!

★★★★★★★★

Find these words from the story in this word search.

Word Box	
basketball	fun
game	play
indoors	school
students	teacher
goals	net
gymnasium	rim

```
B G O A K B O O N T S
A O V T E A C H E R D
L A E C H S E T T E S
I L Y O O K U N I O L
N S T U D E N T S M A
D O A G E T A B I R M
O G L A M B E A F I D
O G Y M N A S I U M U
R E M E P L A Y N O N
S C H O O L R O O S K
```

★Bonus: Find a two-word phrase that means "to reach above the rim and push the ball forcefully through the net."

The Cajuns

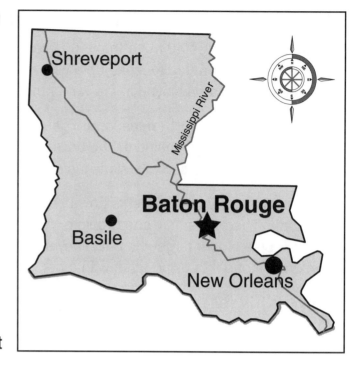

The area known as Acadia lies in the southern part of Louisiana. The people who live here are called Cajuns. They are descended from French settlers who were forced to leave Canada many years ago. Cajuns have been called the happiest people on earth. They are known for their lively music and delicious foods.

A famous festival from this part of the world is the Mardi Gras, which is French for "Fat Tuesday." The most famous Mardi Gras celebration takes place in New Orleans, a large city in Louisiana. But many small towns have their own way of celebrating Mardi Gras. The young men of the town dress in colorful costumes. They ride their horses through the countryside. They go from house to house, asking the people for gifts of food. These food items will be mixed together in a Cajun stew called gumbo. All the townspeople then gather to eat the gumbo, play music, and dance.

Here is a poem about Fat Tuesday.

Fat Tuesday

Fat Tuesday has dawned in the town of Basile
And what an excitement it brings!
The riders are coming. They're dressed up as clowns
Or fabulous monsters with wings.

They're up on their horses and off through the streets
With music and laughter to spare.
They'll beg for some okra, some onions, some shrimp
To make a great gumbo to share.

They come to each house with a shout and a plea
For something to put in the pot.
Tomatoes or peppers or celery stalks,
They're going to need quite a lot!

So everyone gives all that they can afford
And the great gumbo cooking begins.
And the wonderful smell that drifts through the town
Beckons all of the families and friends.

And everyone eats while the music plays on
And they dance and they sing the night through.
Fat Tuesday brings joy to the town of Basile.
How I wish I could be there, don't you?

Celebrating Diversity • EMC 797

Name_____

Questions about *The Cajuns*

1. Many Cajuns live in the state of _____.

2. Mardi Gras means _____.

3. Gumbo is _____.

4. How is Mardi Gras celebrated in some small towns?

_____

_____

_____

5. Would you like to celebrate Fat Tuesday in Basile? Tell why or why not.

_____

_____

_____

6. Describe a fun festival or holiday celebration that takes place in your city or town. What is it? How is it celebrated?

_____

_____

_____

_____

Name_____

The Cajuns
Vocabulary

Label each picture using a word from
the Word Box.

Word Box		
sing	onion	tomatoes
peppers	celery	shrimp

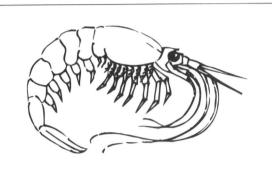

_____

_____

_____

_____

_____

_____

Celebrating Diversity • EMC 797

Name_____

The Cajuns
My Mardi Gras Costume

Pretend that you are going to take part in the Fat Tuesday celebration described in the poem. Draw a picture of the costume you would like to wear.

Name_____

The Cajuns
Rhyming Words

A. Think of three words that rhyme with each word below.

pot	play	cook	fun
_____	_____	_____	_____
_____	_____	_____	_____
_____	_____	_____	_____

B. Write a short poem using some of your rhyming words.

_____

_____

_____

_____

_____

_____

_____

Mollee's Story

Mollee's arm hurt. Her new prosthesis was heavy and she hated wearing it. The artificial limb didn't even look real. It certainly didn't feel real. Why was her dad making her wear it? She knew that he wanted things to be easier for her. But an artificial arm wasn't easier. Mollee was born without part of her right arm. She had accepted it, why couldn't everyone else? She only felt different when she saw the reactions of others.

"The rest of the world has the problem, not me," Mollee thought.

Kids had been mean at her old school. One group of boys in particular were always cruel. They'd push Mollee and call her names. Just because she was missing part of her right arm, they thought she was weak. Other kids would just ignore her. She didn't know what was worse.

Once she'd been talking to a girl from another class at recess. Then the girl noticed her arm. Mollee could see it in her eyes. Something had changed. She stared down at her arms, then looked away. All of a sudden their cheery conversation was over.

But that was her old school. She was ready for a new school, a new start. This time she met her teacher before school started. Her parents let her share her concerns.

"I don't want any special treatment," Mollee assured Mrs. Riley.

"What would you think about sharing the story of your disability with the rest of the class?" Mrs. Riley inquired.

"Mrs. Riley, I'd really rather not. I've found that kids respond to me better if they are able to question me on their own when they're ready," Mollee said.

"Very well then. It sounds as if you've got the situation under control," Mrs. Riley responded.

Today was the first day of school. As she approached the school grounds, butterflies danced the tango in her stomach. But even with this nervousness, Mollee felt a new sense of confidence. "I can do this. I can do this," she repeated to herself over and over. Just then, a petite brown-haired girl approached her.

"Are you new here? I don't remember you from last year," she inquired.

"Oh great," Mollee thought, "here we go again. She knows she'd remember someone who was missing part of her arm and wearing a plastic one." Mollee told herself to stay confident and replied with a smile, "Actually, I just moved here over the summer. I really like it here so far."

"I've lived here all my life. We don't get many new kids, so I hope that we can be friends."

"I'd like that," replied Mollee. "I absolutely despised my old school. The kids were horrible. They had trouble accepting kids that were different."

"That doesn't make sense—we're all different."

Those words echoed in Mollee's brain. Is this girl for real? Mollee sure hoped that she was. On the way to their homeroom, Mollee introduced herself and found out that her new friend's name was Jenaya. As if reading her mind, Jenaya casually asked Mollee what had happened to her arm. She asked as though it were no big deal. Just as casually as she'd been asked, Mollee told her that she was born that way. Jenaya seemed satisfied and told Mollee that she was born with very curly hair. Every day she wished she'd been born with straight hair. Things were definitely off to a great start, but Mollee was guardedly optimistic.

All day she kept waiting for the bomb to drop, but it didn't. The kids at this new school were very accepting and mature. That night at dinner her parents quizzed her about her first day. Mollee looked her father in the eye and told him it had been great. The hardest part, she told them, was having to wear the prosthesis. After thinking about it a moment, Mollee's dad said that wearing the prosthesis was her decision. Mollee jumped out of her chair and gave her dad a big hug. Maybe the rest of the world didn't have such a big problem after all.

Name_____

Questions about *Mollee's Story*

1. Why did Mollee dislike wearing her prosthesis?

_____

_____

2. Mollee waited **for the bomb to drop.** What did she mean when she thought this?

_____

_____

3. Mollee had mixed feelings about her first day of school. What were they?

_____

_____

4. How are Mollee and Jenaya similar? How are they different?

_____

_____

5. The kids at Mollee's new school **are accepting and mature.** What do you think this means?

_____

_____

Name_____

Mollee's Story
Vocabulary

Use the words in the box to complete the sentences in the story below.

Word Box				
prosthesis	inquired	petite	confident	despised
optimistic	casually	satisfied	cruel	

Mollee disliked wearing her _____. In fact, she

_____ the artificial arm. She was glad that her dad wasn't

making her wear it any more. He was _____ with her reasons

for not wanting to wear it. Now she felt _____ as she left for

school.

Kids at her old school had been _____ to her, but she

knew things would be different. In fact, she felt very _____

that kids would be better here. A _____ brown-haired girl

approached her.

"Are you new here?" she _____.

Mollee answered, "Yes, I went to another school last year." She then

_____ raised her arm to see the girl's reaction. Mollee was

surprised when the girl didn't seem to notice.

"I hope we can be friends," the girl said.

"I would like that," Mollee replied.

Name_____

Mollee

Mollee's Story
Help Through Technology

A **prosthesis** is a replacement for a body part because of injury, disease, or a birth defect. It could replace a limb, tooth, or another part of the body. There are three purposes for a prosthesis:

1. It can do the job of the missing part.

2. It provides support for other muscles and bones.

3. It improves the person's appearance.

In the story, Mollee had a prosthesis for her arm. Her prosthesis was mainly worn for appearance.

With today's technology, prosthetic devices have been improved greatly. Materials are lighter and more realistic in appearance. They allow the person wearing them greater flexibility. Prostheses provide people opportunities to participate in sports such as skiing, basketball, and even running.

Here is a list of some prosthetic devices. Decide which of the three purposes above each serves. It could serve one, two, or all three.

Example: arm—**1, 3**

1. false teeth   _____   6. pacemaker   _____

2. artificial heart   _____   7. voice restoration device   _____

3. hearing aid   _____   8. knee replacement   _____

4. kidney transplant _____   9. synthetic arteries and veins _____

5. hairpiece   _____

Name_____

Mollee's Story
Would You Change?

We are all different. We have different looks, opinions, and feelings. This is what makes us unique and special.

If you could change anything about yourself, what would it be? How would you go about changing whatever it is? How do you think changing it would make your life different? Do you think it would be better? Why or why not?

_____

_____

_____

_____

_____

_____

_____

_____

_____

_____

_____

_____

_____

_____

Have you ever wanted something so bad you'd do anything to get it? Hideo Nomo did. He wanted to be a professional baseball player. Hideo worked hard every day to achieve this goal. He even dreamed about baseball. This dedication would pay off.

From the day he was born, Hideo Nomo was different. Hideo was born on August 31, 1968, in Osaka, Japan. He was a big baby by Japanese standards. He weighed 8 pounds 1/2 ounce. His parents thought he might be a sumo wrestler, not a baseball player. His name, pronounced Hee-deh-oh No-mo, has two different meanings. It means "superb" and "man." It also means "hero." Hideo's parents hoped their son would bring joy and honor to the family.

Just like any other kid, Hideo liked to play catch with his father. Every day, when his father got home from work, they'd go to the park. Hideo would drop everything to play baseball. His father, Shizuo, taught him everything he knew about baseball. Soon Hideo's father could no longer help him with baseball. Hideo had advanced beyond his father.

Hideo was a big kid with a big appetite. He loved to eat. His father wanted him to grow strong. His mother, Kayoko, prepared dishes like unagi (eel) and sakana (fish). These foods were rich in vitamin A. Shizuo knew that vitamin A would make Hideo healthier.

When Hideo was in second grade he got a very special gift. His parents bought him his first baseball glove. Hideo put all of his energy into baseball. Every spare moment he had was spent practicing. His parents worried about him because he didn't seem interested in school. In Japan, being the best in school is very important. They got him tutors to help keep his grades up.

A neighbor noticed Hideo's talent. He encouraged him to go out for Little League. In fifth grade Hideo made the team. Soon he was the pitcher for the Ikeshima Fire. Because baseball in Japan came from America, teams often have American names. Team names include the Giants, the Hawks, and the Dragons.

In sixth grade Hideo had to write an essay. He wrote about what he wanted to be when he grew up. What Hideo wrote was no surprise. He wanted to be a professional baseball pitcher.

Hideo was very talented. His talent was almost not enough. Unlike the United States, in Japan you have to take a test to get into high school. If you do well, you get into the best school. Hideo wanted to get into the school with the best baseball team. He failed the test and didn't get in. If he didn't play baseball in high school, he probably wouldn't get to play professionally. He studied even harder and did get into another high school. They had a pretty good team. Hideo pitched for them.

After high school Hideo played in the Japanese minor leagues. He wasn't their starting pitcher at first. He had to practice hard and prove himself. This hard work paid off. He earned a spot on the Japanese Olympic baseball team. In 1988 he competed in the Olympics in Seoul, South Korea.

Then his childhood dream came true. Hideo was drafted to play for a professional baseball team in Japan. Coaches in Japan are very strict. Spring training there is more like an army boot camp. Players are expected to act respectably. They must work hard.

There are twelve professional baseball teams in Japan. They aren't named for the city they're in, as American teams are. Instead they're named for the companies that own them. At the games, the stadium announcers are usually women.

A star was born. Hideo's pitching style soon earned him a nickname. His whirling wind-up reminded people of a tornado. Hideo was known as the "Tornado" when he took the mound. Soon he was earning over a million dollars a year. For Hideo it wasn't about money. He wanted to play in America.

Japanese fans were shocked when he retired from baseball there in 1994. He left to play baseball in America. They didn't understand why he wanted to do this. Hideo became only the second Japanese baseball player in the American major leagues. The first team he played for was the Los Angeles Dodgers. Hideo spoke very little English. An interpreter helped him communicate.

Hideo's language barrier didn't hurt him on the field. He was soon making baseball history. In his first year Hideo was chosen as 1995 National League Rookie of the Year. He also became the first Japanese player chosen to play in a major league All Star game.

Hideo Nomo worked hard. He achieved his lifelong goal—to be a professional baseball player. Two nations, Japan and America, share this baseball hero. Today he competes with the best baseball players in the world. Hideo Nomo found out that if you work hard, dreams do come true.

Name_____

Questions about *Hideo Nomo*

1. Hideo Nomo's dream was to play professional baseball. How did he make this dream come true?

_____

_____

2. How do you think Hideo Nomo was different from other kids? How was he the same as other kids?

_____

_____

3. What is Hideo Nomo's nickname and how did he get it?

_____

_____

4. How did Hideo Nomo communicate with his American teammates?

_____

_____

5. What was more important than money to Hideo?

_____

_____

Name_____

Hideo Nomo
Which Word Means the Same?

Write the word from the box that means the same as the underlined words or phrase in each sentence.

Word Box			
professional	dedication	respectably	compete
barrier	interpreter	achieve	

1. My broken leg was the <u>only thing in my way</u> that kept me from winning.

_____

2. Baseball players in Japan are expected to act <u>with high standards</u>.

_____

3. Hideo played baseball in high school, and then he became a <u>person who plays for money</u>.

_____

4. Dad wants to finish college, and I think he will <u>accomplish</u> this goal.

_____

5. The players' <u>hard work and effort</u> showed in their winning season.

_____

6. Because Maria didn't speak English, she needed a <u>person who spoke her language</u>.

_____

7. She wanted to <u>contend</u> with her class to see who would get the best grade in spelling.

_____

Name_____

Hideo Nomo
Write an Autobiography

The story about Hideo Nomo is a **biography**. A biography is a person's history written by someone else. An **autobiography** is a written history also, but it's written by the person himself or herself.

What have been important events in your life? Do you have any interesting stories about your family? What are your interests, hobbies, and pets? Where were you born?

Write your autobiography in the space below. Use more paper if you need to.

_____

_____

_____

_____

_____

_____

_____

_____

_____

_____

_____

_____

Name_____

Hideo Nomo
What a Card!

Baseball cards are traded all over the world. Hideo Nomo's baseball card is very popular. A baseball card is a record of a player's career. It includes a picture of the player and information about his personal life. Make your own baseball card. Be sure to draw a picture of yourself.

Name: _____

Birthday: _____

Height: _____

Weight: _____

Age: _____

Hometown: _____

School: _____

Favorite Author: _____

Favorite Book: _____

Future Goal: _____

May 27, 1987, started out as an ordinary day. Kalen went to school as usual and came home around 3:30 P.M. She played with her neighborhood buddies. Kalen was having a carefree, end-of-the-school-year evening. All that changed later in the night when Kalen began to feel sick to her stomach and extremely dizzy.

The next thing she remembered was waking up in the hospital. She was unable to move the left side of her body. Her head hurt. Words she used so freely were struggling to come out of her mouth. Kalen's mom and the doctors tried to explain that she had a stroke. Didn't strokes just happen to old people? How could it have happened to her? She was only thirteen years old!

For the next three months Kalen lived at the hospital. Every day was so hard. Things that had been automatic were now a struggle. Trying to pick up a spoon and raise it to her mouth, lifting a leg, holding a ball, or wiggling her toes seemed so difficult. A therapist came twice a day. He worked with her to keep her muscles from weakening. Another therapist came to help Kalen with her speech. Some days she just wanted to give up and say, "No more!" Thank goodness Kalen never stopped trying.

The therapy did not stop when Kalen went home. She still went to the hospital twice a day for care. Things were getting better, but Kalen still wasn't the way she used to be. The doctors said that would take a lot more time.

Then the new school year started. The first day of school was always so exciting. But Kalen was scared and didn't want to leave her house. What would the kids say when they saw her? Would they ask why her face sagged a little on the left side? What about the way her arm shook and looked as if she were carrying something? Would they say something about the way her left leg needed to be lifted higher than the right leg? Kalen was certain that everyone would be staring at her all day long.

Fortunately Kalen's teachers were ready to help. They explained about what a stroke does to your brain and to the muscles in your body. A lot of students did stare, but by lunchtime Kalen didn't feel quite so anxious. For the most part, everyone was helpful. One of her friends handed her a letter right before third class.

Dear Kalen,

I am happy that you are back at school. I know things were hard for you this summer. Please let me help if you need anything.

It's great to have you back!

Brandi

At afternoon recess Kalen watched her friends play soccer. She wanted to be out there too. Soccer was a passion for Kalen. It was what she loved more than anything. She was determined to play again. She decided to work even harder at all her therapies.

Therapy continued twice a day. Every night Kalen practiced kicking the soccer ball. Running was hard, but each day she was stronger and faster. By spring Kalen felt ready to try out for the team. She didn't make it. But Kalen didn't let the disappointment get to her for too long. She started to prepare for the next season the following day. She was more determined than ever.

When therapy was reduced to once a day, Kalen exercised on her own for an extra hour. She could now kick a ball almost as hard as before the stroke. Her left arm was straighter. Her speed was almost at the pre-stroke level. Having worked this hard, she wasn't about to give up!

One year later Kalen made the high school junior varsity soccer team. She had become a stronger person. She had learned to appreciate the little things that many people take for granted— walking, talking, writing, and kicking a soccer ball. A painful experience had turned into a positive lesson about dedication and determination. Never before had she felt so proud of herself.

Questions about *The Road to Recovery*

1. What happened to Kalen on May 27, 1987?

_____

2. Name two or three things that were hard for Kalen to do after she had
a stroke.

_____

_____

3. Why wasn't Kalen excited about starting school in September?

_____

_____

4. Choose one word that best describes Kalen. _____

Use examples from the story to support your word choice.

_____

_____

5. What does **take for granted** mean in this sentence?

   She had learned to appreciate the little things that many people
   take for granted.

_____

_____

6. What lesson can you learn from Kalen?

_____

_____

Name_____

The Road to Recovery
Vocabulary

Read the sentences below. Look for clues that will help you find the meaning of each underlined word. Fill in the correct circle.

1. It was an <u>ordinary</u> school day in May.
   ○ regular   ○ not typical   ○ exciting

2. Things that had once been so <u>automatic</u> were now a daily struggle.
   ○ firearm   ○ shifting   ○ routine

3. Soccer had always been a <u>passion</u> for Kalen.
   ○ need   ○ resentment   ○ love

4. After the stroke, her face <u>sagged</u> on one side.
   ○ curved   ○ drooped   ○ straightened

5. By lunchtime she didn't feel quite so <u>anxious</u>.
   ○ energetic   ○ angry   ○ worried

6. The afternoon was quite <u>carefree</u>.
   ○ relaxed   ○ hot   ○ eventful

7. She was more <u>determined</u> than ever to make the team.
   ○ ready   ○ intent on   ○ uncaring

8. <u>Fortunately</u> the teachers were very helpful.
   ○ richly   ○ naturally   ○ luckily

The Road to Recovery
Tell About Kalen

Complete the character map about Kalen. Write facts from the story to support each heading.

Determined	Anxious	Proud
	didn't want to start school wondered what all her classmates might say	

Kalen

Athletic	Hardworking	Disappointed

Name_____

The Road to Recovery
Brainy Information

The **brain** is the main organ of our **nervous system**. It is located at the upper end of the spinal cord. It is enclosed by the skull. The brain is made up of thousands of nerves. It controls all of our actions—those we decide to do, such as speaking, and those that are automatic, such as breathing. The brain is the center of memory, learning, and emotion. No computer is as complex as our human brain.

1. Which of these would be the best resource for information about the brain?

   ○ dictionary   ○ thesaurus   ○ atlas   ○ encyclopedia

2. You could look under **B** in an encyclopedia to get information about the brain. From what you read in the paragraph above, what letter might you look under next to find more information? Circle the letter and explain your choice.

A B C D E F G H I J K L M N O P Q R S T U V W X Y Z

_____

_____

3. Circle the correct answer.

   The brain controls only voluntary actions such as speaking.   True   False

   The brain is located at the upper end of our spinal cord.   True   False

   The brain is more complex than any computer.   True   False

   The brain is made up of thousands of nerves.   True   False

   The brain pumps blood throughout our body.   True   False

Ben Nighthorse Campbell is Native American. He's the only Native American serving in the United States Congress. Ben's father Albert was Cheyenne Indian. Ben was born on April 13, 1933.

For much of his life he didn't know a lot about his Native American heritage. When Ben was growing up, there were many negative feelings about Native Americans. Movies showed Indians as cruel, violent, and dishonest. These same movies made the white people look smarter and better than the Indians. These pictures affected Ben's life.

Ben's father encouraged him to hide his Cheyenne roots. Ben never felt comfortable doing this, but he didn't know what else to do. Ben was able to pass as non-Indian. His last name didn't give away the secret. Many Native Americans took "white" names from their employers. They did this to fit in a white people's world. Ben thinks this is how his family got the name Campbell.

Ben's young years were hard. His parents had many troubles. Ben's father was discriminated against at work and in the community. He became an alcoholic. Ben's mother had tuberculosis. This disease made her unable to work or care for her family. Ben and his sister had to live for a while in a children's home.

Ben never forgot what it was like to live in the children's home. He felt alone and scared. He didn't like strangers raising him. He was angry, especially with his father.

At the age of nine, Ben went to work to help the family. One of Ben's jobs was working in the fields. There he learned judo from Japanese American children who worked in the fields with him. He watched them use judo to defend themselves. Like him, their appearance and background often kept them from being accepted.

In school Ben was popular and athletic. He didn't care about studying. He quit high school to join the Air Force and served in the Korean War. During this time he finished his high school studies.

After the war Ben entered San Jose State College in California. He joined the judo team and made fast progress in the sport. With Ben's help, the team won many championships. To improve his judo skills, Ben moved to Japan. There he studied the martial arts for four years. This training paid off. In 1963 he won the gold medal for judo at the Pan American games.

Ben Nighthorse Campbell was an adult before he recognized his Native American heritage. In 1976 Ben became a member of the Cheyenne Nation. He was also given a Cheyenne name. He would be called "Night Horse," after his great-grandfather. The name is spelled as one word— Nighthorse.

Ben sees himself as a voice for Native Americans. Not long after being elected to Congress, he had a painting removed from the capitol building. The painting showed a Native American scalping a white man. Ben thought this was in bad taste.

Ben is always an individual first. He fought the dress code of Congress and won. Members were expected to wear suits and ties. Ben wanted this rule changed. He preferred boots and bolo ties.

Senator Ben Nighthorse Campbell takes great pride in his Cheyenne ancestry. He votes for laws that protect Native Americans and other minorities. He works hard to educate people and to stop discrimination.

Name_____

Questions about *Ben Nighthorse Campbell*

1. Why do you think Ben didn't feel comfortable about hiding his Native American heritage?

_____

_____

2. Campbell is not a Native American name. Where did Ben's family get this last name?

_____

_____

3. Who first inspired Ben's interest in the martial arts? How did they inspire him?

_____

_____

_____

4. How can you tell that Ben is a determined person?

_____

_____

5. The story says, "Ben is always an individual first." What do you think that means?

_____

_____

Name_____

Ben Nighthorse Campbell
Word Meaning

Write the word from the Word Box that matches each definition.

Word Box	
athletic	negative
cruel	minorities
heritage	discrimination
preferred	recognized

1. accepted; approved of

___ ___ ___ ___ ___ ___ ___ ___ ___
                 14 4

2. something handed down from past generations

___ ___ ___ ___ ___ ___ ___ ___
            2

3. not positive

___ ___ ___ ___ ___ ___ ___ ___
 1   7   5

4. mean; causing pain

___ ___ ___ ___ ___
12   6

5. an act based on viewing others as not equal

___ ___ ___ ___ ___ ___ ___ ___ ___ ___ ___ ___ ___ ___
           11   3

6. parts of the population that differ from others

___ ___ ___ ___ ___ ___ ___ ___ ___ ___
 8

7. physically skilled

___ ___ ___ ___ ___ ___ ___ ___
13

8. liked more

___ ___ ___ ___ ___ ___ ___ ___ ___
         10   9

Solve the puzzle. Match each numbered letter above with the same number in the puzzle.

Clue: Ben Nighthorse Campbell is the only one in the United States Congress.

___ ___ ___ ___ ___ ___   ___ ___ ___ ___ ___ ___ ___ ___
1   2   3   4   5   6   7   8   9 10 11 12 13 14

Name_____

Ben Nighthorse Campbell
Determination

Determination means the ability to stay focused on your goal and the will to keep working to achieve it.

In almost every story you have read about well-known people, the word **determination** was used. You could tell that Ben Nighthorse Campbell is determined by the way he worked to become a top martial artist and by how he continues to work to stop discrimination.

- What would you like to do in your life that will require determination?

- How will you stay focused on this goal?

- What will you have to do to achieve your goal?

_____

_____

_____

_____

_____

_____

_____

_____

_____

Ben Nighthorse Campbell
Job Skills

Ben Nighthorse Campbell has had many different jobs in his life. Think of words to describe the responsibilities of each of these jobs and the qualities it takes to do the job. Then complete a word web for each job.

The first one has been done as an example.

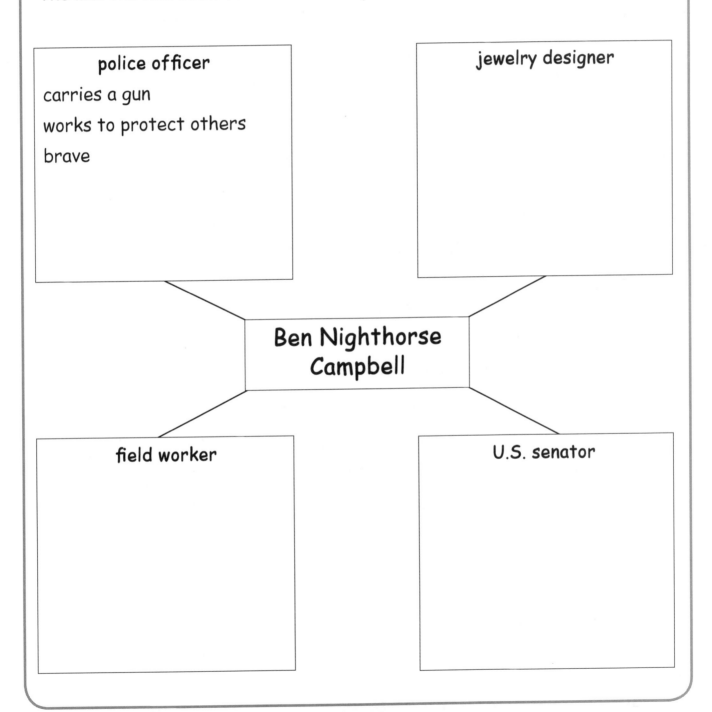

police officer

carries a gun

works to protect others

brave

jewelry designer

Ben Nighthorse Campbell

field worker

U.S. senator

Kwanzaa

Jambo, rafiki! (Hello, friends!) Let's learn about Kwanzaa!

Kwanzaa is a celebration for African Americans. It was begun in 1966 by Dr. Maulana Karenga (Mah oo lan' nah Kar ren' gah). He thought that the lives of African Americans would be enriched by honoring their African heritage. Over 13 million Americans of African descent celebrate Kwanzaa. For seven days they take pride in African culture and the importance of family.

As with many festivals, lights play an important part. Each night from December 26 until January 1 a candle is lit. The candles are placed in a special holder called a kinara. There is a black candle, three red candles, and three green candles. Each candle represents one of the seven principles of Kwanzaa:

Unity—helping each other

Self-determination—being in control of one's own life

Collective work and responsibility—working together to make a better life

Cooperative economics—sharing money and profits

Purpose—having goals for one's life

Creativity—using the hands and mind to make things

Faith—believing in one's self and the future

During Kwanzaa many families dress in brightly colored clothes with designs rooted in African art. Families make handmade gifts to give as presents. They create masks, read African stories, and eat special meals. It is a happy time for loved ones to gather together. For many African Americans it's also a great way to say good-bye to the old year and ring in the new!

Kwanzaa yenu iwe na heri!
May your Kwanzaa be a happy one!

Name_____

Questions about *Kwanzaa*

1. Who is the person responsible for creating Kwanzaa?

   _____

2. In what year was Kwanzaa first celebrated?

   _____

3. Explain what the third principle of Kwanzaa (collective work and responsibility) means to you.

   _____

   _____

   _____

4. For each night of Kwanzaa a candle is lit. Why?

   _____

   _____

5. Name three things you could do to celebrate Kwanzaa.

   _____

   _____

   _____

6. What does **Jambo, rafiki** mean in English?

   _____

Name_____

Kwanzaa
Vocabulary

A. Use these words to complete the sentences below.

heritage	faith	pride	descent
future	principles	ancestors	accomplishments

1. My _____ are from Africa.

2. We must make our plans now to prepare for the _____.

3. African Americans take _____ in their culture.

4. Creating masks, reading stories, and making handmade gifts are part of

my African _____.

5. An African American is of African _____.

6. Dr. Karenga explained the seven _____ of Kwanzaa.

7. Kwanzaa is a happy time for families to be proud of their

_____.

8. I have _____ that this will be a good new year.

B. During Kwanzaa many families dress in brightly colored clothes with designs **rooted** in African art. What is a synonym for the word **rooted**?

○ grown   ○ positioned   ○ originated   ○ dug up

Name_____

Kwanzaa
Praising Myself

Write about the accomplishments you are proud of and your goals for the future.

Accomplishments

_____

_____

_____

_____

_____

_____

Goals

_____

_____

_____

_____

_____

_____

_____

Name_____

Kwanzaa
Read the Grid

On the grid below are some symbols that stand for ideas about Kwanzaa. Write the coordinate pairs that tell where each picture is located. The first one has been done for you.

1. Flag of Nigeria   __2, 5__   4. Drum   _____

2. Map of Africa   _____   5. Corn   _____

3. Fruit   _____   6. Candles   _____

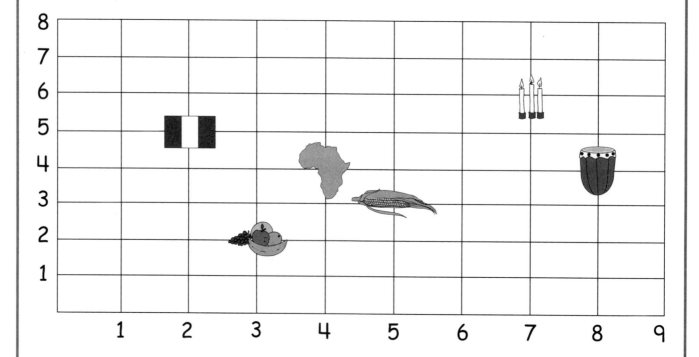

Draw another Kwanzaa symbol somewhere on the grid.

Describe your symbol. _____

Write its coordinate pair. _____

Jackie Robinson was born in Georgia in 1919. He was the youngest of five children. When Jackie was only six months old, his mother moved her family to Pasadena, California, to find a better life for her family.

Jackie didn't have much time for playing while he was growing up. His family was poor. He had to help out by delivering papers, running errands, and cutting lawns. On weekends Jackie sold hot dogs at a nearby baseball stadium. There, Jackie noticed something that bothered him. There were no black players on any of the teams.

In high school Jackie played basketball, football, and baseball, and ran track. After high school he went to the University of California at Los Angeles. At UCLA Jackie won awards in all four of those sports. He was the first person ever to do this.

Jackie left UCLA in 1941 and was drafted into the army. While in the army, he was faced with unfairness. He wanted to join the army football and baseball teams. Because he was black, he could not do so.

Jackie left the army after almost three years. In 1945 he began playing baseball with the Kansas City Monarchs. This was a team in the Negro American League. Even though he was a very skilled player, he could not play in the major leagues. Major league baseball still hired only white players.

But a brave man named Branch Rickey was about to change all that. Rickey was the president of the Brooklyn Dodgers. He signed Jackie Robinson to play for the Dodgers' minor league team, the Montreal Royals. The year was 1946. The next year Rickey signed Jackie to play second base for the Brooklyn Dodgers.

It took a lot of courage to stick it out as the first black player in major league baseball. Many players and fans did not want him to play. But determination and skill paid off. He was named Rookie of the Year in 1947. In 1949 he was named Most Valuable Player. In 1955 Jackie Robinson helped the Brooklyn Dodgers win their first World Series.

Jackie Robinson was a great man. He helped pave the way for other black players to play in the major leagues. In 1962 Jackie Robinson was honored again. This time he became the first black American to be voted into baseball's Hall of Fame. No one deserved this honor more than Jackie Robinson. He was truly one of the greatest baseball players of all time. Jackie Robinson died in 1972. He was 53 years old.

Name_____

Questions about *Jackie Robinson*

1. Choose the word that best describes Jackie Robinson.

   ○ smart   ○ truthful   ○ shy   ○ brave

2. Jackie Robinson was a gifted athlete.   ○ True   ○ False
   Explain your answer.

   _____

   _____

3. What does the author mean when she says that it took a lot of courage for
   Jackie to **stick it out** being the first black player in professional baseball?

   _____

   _____

   _____

4. Name one person you think probably had a big influence on Jackie
   Robinson. Explain your answer.

   _____

   _____

   _____

5. What lesson can you learn from Jackie Robinson?

   _____

   _____

   _____

Name_____

Jackie Robinson
Word Meaning

Write the number of each word on the line in front of its meaning.

1. determination   _____ a group of teams

2. unfairness   _____ state of being well known; renown

3. fame   _____ of great importance

4. valuable   _____ sticking to a purpose

5. league   _____ selected for military service

6. drafted   _____ lack of justice

Adding Prefixes and Suffixes

un means **not**	**ful** means **full of**	**pre** means **before**

Add the correct prefix or suffix.

1. before the season   _____season

2. full of hope   hope_____

3. not equal   _____equal

4. tell about in advance   _____dict

5. not fair   _____fair

6. full of wonder   wonder_____

7. not happy   _____happy

Name_____

Jackie Robinson
Making Comparisons

Compare yourself and Jackie Robinson using the Venn diagram.

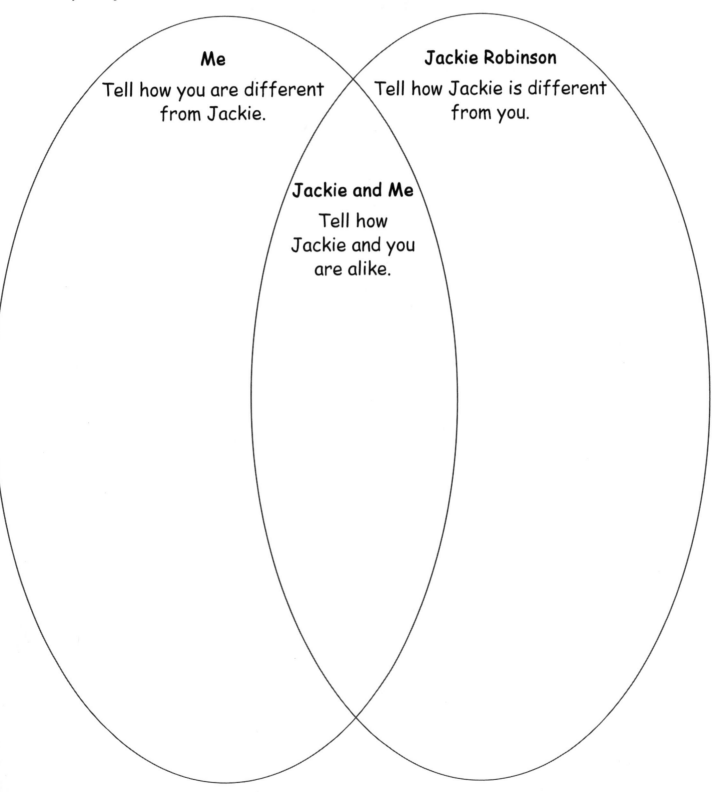

Me
Tell how you are different from Jackie.

Jackie Robinson
Tell how Jackie is different from you.

Jackie and Me
Tell how Jackie and you are alike.

Name_____

Jackie Robinson
Graphing Baseballs

Baseballs Used in a Game

Monday	⚾	⚾	⚾	⚾	⚾	⚾	
Tuesday	⚾	⚾	⚾	⚾	⚾		
Wednesday	⚾	⚾	⚾	⚾	⚾	⚾	⚾
Thursday	⚾	⚾	⚾	⚾			
Friday	⚾	⚾	⚾	⚾	⚾		
Saturday	⚾	⚾	⚾				

Key: ⚾ = 10

1. How many baseballs were used on Thursday? _____

2. Which two days of the week combined equal the same amount of baseballs

   used on Wednesday? _____ and _____

3. How many fewer baseballs were used on Saturday than on Monday?

4. On the lines below, write three statements that you know are true about the graph.

   _____

   _____

   _____

 # Michelle Kwan

Michelle Kwan was born on July 7, 1980, in southern California. Her parents were immigrants from China. They worked hard to make a good life for Michelle and her sister and brother. They believed that America was the place where they could make a good living. It was a place where their children would be happy and healthy. Michelle learned the value of working hard. This lesson would help Michelle achieve her dreams.

As a young girl, Michelle took gymnastics lessons with her sister, Karen. Later she began ice-skating lessons. From the beginning she loved being on ice. She learned how to stand, how to walk on the ice, and how to fall without hurting herself. Then she was ready to tackle the more difficult and fun moves. It didn't take Michelle long to be comfortable on the ice. Skating made her feel as if she were flying.

At age seven and a half, Michelle knew she wanted to be an Olympic champion. That's when she saw Brian Boitano win the skating gold medal for the United States at the Winter Olympics.

Michelle had a lot of determination for one so young. She began training five days a week. There wasn't much time for other activities. When she wasn't practicing, she was doing schoolwork. School was important to Michelle. She always wanted to get good grades.

As skaters get better, they move up through levels of competition. For girls, the final step is to become a senior woman skater. This is the level where the best skaters in the world compete. Michelle knew she needed to be a senior woman skater to be a world champion. She was accepted as a student at a private ice rink known as Ice Castle. She skated all day long, seven days a week. It took a lot of hard work, but Michelle loved the challenge. She became a senior woman skater at age twelve. Then she began skating in national competitions.

In the following years Michelle had many successes, and some big disappointments too. Then in 1998 Michelle finally proved to herself and the world that she was a champion. It was her third time at the U.S. National Championships. This time she was older and more experienced. Her performance went flawlessly. The judges gave her fifteen out of sixteen perfect scores. She took first place. Hard work and determination had finally paid off.

Later that year Michelle skated to a silver medal at the Winter Olympics in Nagano, Japan. She was second to another U.S. skater, Tara Lipinski.

Michelle Kwan continues to be an artist on ice. She is a great athlete who appreciates life as much as she enjoys the sport of ice-skating. Now she works to balance skating with getting a college education. Michelle Kwan is a champion in every sense of the word.

Name_____

Questions about *Michelle Kwan*

1. Where was Michelle Kwan born?

   ○ China   ○ northern California   ○ southern California   ○ Korea

2. What lessons did Michelle take before she began ice-skating? How might this
   have helped her as a skater?

   _____

   _____

3. What event helped Michelle decide that she wanted to become an
   Olympic skater?

   _____

   _____

4. How do you think Michelle Kwan feels when she is skating on ice?

   _____

   _____

5. Michelle Kwan could be described as **hardworking**. Support this statement
   with two facts from the story.

   _____

   _____

   _____

6. What do the words **her determination paid off** mean to you?

   _____

   _____

Michelle Kwan
Vocabulary

A. Write a synonym (word that means the same) from the box for each vocabulary word found in the story about Michelle Kwan.

Word Box			
undertake	test	contest	persistence
winner	perfectly	at ease	drill

1. comfortable _____

2. challenge _____

3. practice _____

4. determination _____

5. champion _____

6. flawlessly _____

7. tackle _____

8. competition _____

B. Choose two words from the box and use each word in a sentence.

1. _____

_____

2. _____

_____

Name_____

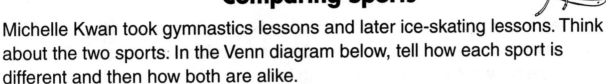

Michelle Kwan took gymnastics lessons and later ice-skating lessons. Think about the two sports. In the Venn diagram below, tell how each sport is different and then how both are alike.

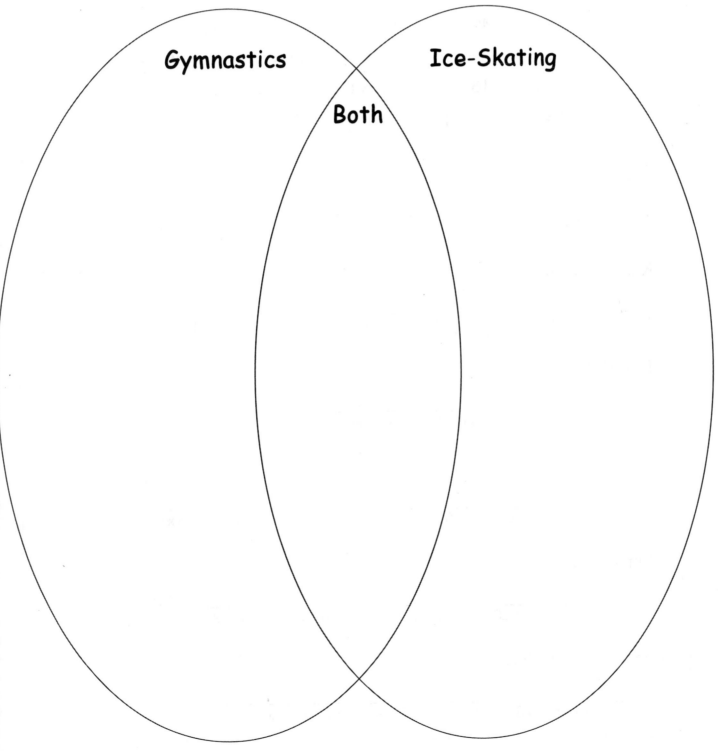

Gymnastics

Both

Ice-Skating

Name_____

Michelle Kwan
Champions Puzzle

The names of the people below are all United States Olympic Champions. Find out what sport each competed in. Solve the math problem under each blank. Then use the answers to fill in the missing letters.

40 = k	42 = a	18 = s	20 = n	12 = o
8 = p	32 = m	14 = e	30 = c	10 = w
24 = i	16 = z	36 = t	4 = u	28 = h
48 = y	2 = j	44 = r	22 = g	6 = l

1. Carl Lewis

$\overline{}$ $\overline{}$ $\overline{}$ $\overline{}$ $\overline{}$
9 x 4   11 x 4   6 x 7   3 x 10   8 x 5

2. Kristi Yamaguchi

$\overline{}$ $\overline{}$ $\overline{}$ $\overline{}$ $\overline{}$ $\overline{}$ $\overline{}$ $\overline{}$ $\overline{}$ $\overline{}$
12 + 12   10 + 20   7 + 7   9 + 9   34 + 6   2 + 40   18 + 18   15 + 9   10 + 10   11 + 11

3. Phil Mahre

$\overline{}$ $\overline{}$ $\overline{}$ $\overline{}$ $\overline{}$ $\overline{}$
24 − 6   50 − 10   30 − 6   36 − 12   60 − 40   44 − 22

4. Mary Lou Retton

$\overline{}$ $\overline{}$ $\overline{}$ $\overline{}$ $\overline{}$ $\overline{}$ $\overline{}$ $\overline{}$ $\overline{}$ $\overline{}$
2 x 11   6 x 8   8 x 4   4 x 5   6 x 7   2 x 9   6 x 6   3 x 8   5 x 6   6 x 3

5. Mark Spitz

$\overline{}$ $\overline{}$ $\overline{}$ $\overline{}$ $\overline{}$ $\overline{}$ $\overline{}$ $\overline{}$
10 + 8   7 + 3   4 + 20   6 + 26   12 + 20   14 + 10   8 + 12   13 + 9

6. Jackie Joyner-Kersee

$\overline{}$ $\overline{}$ $\overline{}$ $\overline{}$ $\overline{}$ $\overline{}$ $\overline{}$ $\overline{}$
10 − 4   18 − 6   25 − 5   44 − 22   29 − 27   13 − 9   36 − 4   16 − 8

Can getting into trouble at school change the course of a person's life? For Thurgood Marshall the answer is "yes." As punishment for talking too much, his teacher sent him to the school basement to read the Constitution of the United States.

Thurgood Marshall used this experience as a wonderful chance to learn. And learn is what he did! He memorized the entire Constitution and could explain its meaning by the time he was finished with grade school.

He studied the Fourteenth Amendment the hardest. It said that all citizens have equal rights. As a black American he knew he did not have equal rights. Black people were not allowed to buy houses in "white" neighborhoods. They were not allowed to eat at certain restaurants. Drinking fountains were marked "colored" or "white." Schools were segregated. That meant black people were not permitted to attend the same schools as white people. Thurgood Marshall was confused. How could these things happen when the Constitution promised *all* people equal rights? He decided then that he would help change things when he grew older.

In 1925 Thurgood Marshall attended Lincoln University in Pennsylvania. This was the country's oldest "black" college. He studied hard and decided to become a lawyer. In 1929 Marshall began law school at Howard University in Washington, D.C.

He admired many of his black professors and listened to their words very carefully. They taught him to always be prepared and to work toward excellence. This is what he did! Thurgood Marshall was the top student in his class at graduation.

In 1933 Thurgood Marshall began practicing law. He opened a small office in Baltimore, Maryland. Most of the people who came to see him were poor black people. They could not afford to pay him much money. He helped everyone who came to see him.

Marshall also began to work with the NAACP.* The people in this group were committed to ending segregation. For many years Thurgood Marshall traveled the country arguing court cases against segregation. He became known as one of the best lawyers in the nation.

But laws in some states still allowed segregation. Thurgood Marshall knew that more would have to be done. He felt that segregation would end only through education. If children had a good education, they could improve themselves and their lives. He also believed that black and white children needed to be educated together. This would help them learn to appreciate differences rather than hate.

In 1953 Thurgood Marshall took an important law case to the United States Supreme Court. It was called Brown v. the Board of Education. Marshall proved that segregated schools were not equal. He proved that the number of teachers and the amounts of money given to the schools

*National Association for the Advancement of Colored People

were not the same. He proved that segregation caused black children to feel second-rate. This made them less interested in learning. Then they did not reach their highest potential. The Supreme Court decided that segregated schools were unequal. This was one of Thurgood Marshall's greatest achievements.

Thurgood Marshall did not stop fighting for justice. President John F. Kennedy gave Marshall an important judgeship. In 1967 President Lyndon B. Johnson appointed Marshall to the United States Supreme Court. He was the first black American on the highest court in the land. Thurgood Marshall served as a judge on the U.S. Supreme Court until 1991.

Thurgood Marshall was a great man who worked hard to make our country a better place to live. He fought for the rights of all Americans. He was eighty-four years old when he died on January 24, 1993.

Name_____

Questions about *Thurgood Marshall*

1. How did Thurgood Marshall happen to learn about the Constitution of the United States of America?

_____

_____

2. What words of the Fourteenth Amendment did Thurgood Marshall study hardest?

_____

3. What really bothered Thurgood Marshall as he was learning about the Constitution? Give two examples.

_____

_____

_____

4. What did the United States Supreme Court decide about segregated schools?

_____

_____

5. Do you go to a segregated or an integrated school? Explain your answer.

_____

_____

_____

Name_____

Thurgood Marshall
Vocabulary

A. Write each word from the box on the line next to its meaning.

Word Box			
segregate	memorize	potential	equal
appreciate	argue	appointed	achievement

1. having the same rights _____

2. to present reasons to support an opinion _____

3. to keep apart from others _____

4. selected for a position _____

5. to realize the worth of something _____

6. possibility _____

7. to learn by heart _____

8. something accomplished _____

B. What does the word **committed** mean in this sentence?

Thurgood Marshall was **committed** to ending segregation.

○ saddened   ○ careful   ○ dedicated   ○ afraid

Name_____

Thurgood Marshall
Now and Then

Draw a picture of your school today.

Tell how your school is different from the school Thurgood Marshall attended when he was young.

_____

_____

_____

_____

Name_____

Thurgood Marshall
A Time Line

Use information from the story. Write an event in Thurgood Marshall's life for each year on the time line.

1909	
1925	
1929	
1933	
1953	
1967	
1991	
1993	

★Bonus: Try making a time line of your own life on another sheet of paper. Start with the year you were born and add important dates. Ask your family for help.

D oes it matter to you what color

I am? Or what kind of

V ehicle I drive?

E ach of us is different, but we must show

R espect and

S ensitivity.

I want to work with you.

T ake my hand.

Y ou and I can make a difference.

Name_____

Diversity
Picturing Diversity

Draw to show what the word **diversity** means to you. Include as much detail as you can to support your idea.

Write to explain what is happening in your picture.

_____

_____

_____

Answer Key

Page 7

1. She likes the rows of pretty packages. She loves how shiny and neat everything is. Students may infer that she also enjoys being able to help her mom.

2. Jimmy's mother turned red and pulled on his shirt to divert his attention and told him it wasn't polite to stare. She was embarrassed about what Jimmy had said about Diane's mother. You could tell she was embarrassed because she blushed (turned red).

3. Diane's mom told Jimmy that his behavior was OK and asked him if he'd like to see her wheelchair. Diane's mom was not offended by Jimmy's question. You could tell she was comfortable being looked at in her wheelchair by the way she talked to Jimmy and explained things to him about being handicapped.

4. Diane is proud of her mother and enjoys spending time with her.

Page 8

Answers will vary.

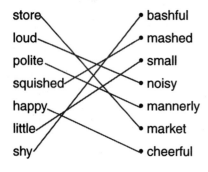

store — market
loud — noisy
polite — mannerly
squished — mashed
happy — cheerful
little — small
shy — bashful

Page 9

Students' responses will vary.

Page 10

1. $3.16
2. $0.60
3. $5.46
4. 8 apples
5. $1.10

Page 15

1. she was not chosen because she was not white; **or** that Sarah Jacobs had been right when she said that Jamie wouldn't get the part because she wasn't white.

2. they would choose her because they knew she was a hard worker.

3. this was strange. She wondered why people thought they looked different from other mothers and daughters.

4. that prejudice had not been the reason she did not get the lead role.

5. they would become friends.

6. was eager to be in the play.

Page 16

1. encouraging
2. bothering
3. amazed
4. opinions
5. brag
6. reject
7. praise
8. difficulty
9. envious
10. needs

Page 17

Students' responses will vary.

Page 18

Students' responses will vary.

Page 22

1. TS is a lifelong disorder. A person with TS has tics, which are uncontrolled, repeated body movements.

2. Students should list at least two of the following: coughing uncontrollably, laughing at inappropriate times, shouting, shoulder shrugging, head jerking, rocking, bumping into things, clapping his hands, and spitting.

3. Answers will vary. Nick doesn't have any friends. He doesn't get any phone calls at home from classmates. He never goes to anyone's house after school. The kids just stare when he's having his tics.

4. Answers will vary. Nick could tell that his classmates understood him better once they asked him questions. They weren't afraid once they knew more about TS.

5. Answers will vary. Nick is hopeful that he and Jeff will become friends. Nick thinks Jeff will understand him because his dad has TS.

Page 23

1. medication — b
2. concentrate — a
3. severe — c
4. treatment — h
5. control — d
6. depressed — g
7. suggest — f
8. curious — e

Page 24

Students' responses will vary. Accept any reasonable, well-thought-out answers.

Page 25

Students' responses will vary. Accept any reasonable, well-thought-out answers.

Page 29

1. The Hmong had fought against the group (Pathet Lao) that gained control of Laos. Their lives were in danger.

2. Answers may include: a language that was hard to learn; modern conveniences such as electric appliances, running water, cars. Also many new smells, tastes, and even different weather.

3. Fresno has always been home to Gao, but the stories his father tells of Laos make him feel it is familiar and like home also.

4. Answers will vary, but should contain the idea that the sounds of English were difficult for her to say.

5. Gao wants to be a teacher so that he can help other immigrants who come to America.

Page 30

1. Refugees are people who must leave their homes because of danger.

2. angry, afraid, happy, sad

3. Choices include: parents, mother, father, relatives, sisters, cousins, aunts, uncles.

4. Drawings will vary.

Page 31

Students' responses will vary.

Page 32

1. Laos, Thailand

2. Laos had been the home of the Hmong; Gao's family fled to safety in Thailand.

3. Choices include: Cambodia, Vietnam, Myanmar (Burma), China.

Page 37

1. They both felt angry and sad about the suffering of the farm workers. Both wanted to do something to help these people.

2. Possible answers: Cesar went to many schools; this made it hard to study and make friends. Teachers got angry with him when he spoke Spanish. He knew that his parents needed help to support the family.

3. Answers may include: low pay, long working hours, crowded living conditions, unsafe drinking water, sickness, hunger.

4. Chavez and Huerta helped the farm workers organize. As a group they can demand safer working conditions, fairer pay, and better living conditions.

Page 38

A. 1. crops
2. grueling
3. champion
4. taxes
5. migrant
6. irrigation
B. 2
3
1

Page 39

Students' responses will vary.

Page 40

abuelo

casa

uvas

dinero

Page 44

1. Answers will vary, but should relay the idea that from that point everyone in the family had to deal with the sad reality that Grandpa would continue to decline in his mental abilities.

2. Benito no longer spent weekends with Grandpa; he couldn't teach him karate moves anymore; Grandpa often did not know who Benito was.

3. 5, 1, 2, 4, 3, 6

Page 45

3, 5, 1, 2, 4

1. farmer: Grandpa looked after Benito *like a farmer tends to his crop.*

2. snowball: Alzheimer's was *like a snowball.*

Page 46

Letters will vary.

Page 47

The cerebrum should be colored gray, the medulla should be colored blue, and the cerebellum should be colored red.

Page 52

1. Laws in southern states that said blacks did not have equal rights.

2. Gandhi believed in changing things through nonviolent protest, not fighting. This idea had worked in India, and Martin Luther King, Jr., thought it could work in the United States as well.

3. Rosa Parks refused to give up her bus seat to a white person. Martin became the leader of a bus boycott to get the bus company to change its practices.

4. He believed that people must let go of hatred; that nonviolence and love would do more than violence and hate to make changes.

5. Martin Luther King, Jr., is remembered for his dream of equal rights for all and his work to make that dream come true.

Page 53

A. 1. take an action against something you believe is wrong
2. at a church
3. to not use
4. idea
5. fight
B. 1. succeed
2. arrested
3. nation

Page 54

Students' responses will vary.

Page 55

1. liberty
2. bravery
3. prison
4. dad
5. fighting

Page 58

1. her husband Mike, 1917

2. The voyage was long and miserable. He was seasick much of the trip.

3. Answers will vary, but may mention the idea of new opportunities and the promise of a better life.

4. Yugoslavia

5. The work was hard and the days were long. English was difficult to learn. Some Americans called him names and did not treat him with respect.

6. He hopes to travel to Oregon and work in the lumber camps. He will save money to send for his wife and son. One day he hopes to have his own business and a nice house.

Page 59

A. 5, 8, 2, 7, 1, 3, 4, 6
B. Illustrations will vary.

Page 60

8
6
3
1
4
2
5
7

Page 61

Students' responses will vary.

Celebrating Diversity • EMC 797

Page 64

1. She was worried that children would laugh at her because she didn't speak English.

2. nervous to relaxed

3. They were migrant workers who traveled around to work on different farms.

4. Probable answer is Mexico or perhaps another Latin American country. The fact that they spoke Spanish is the most reasonable explanation.

5. Answers will vary.

Page 65

1. a, b	3. b, a	5. b, a
2. b, a	4. b, a	6. a, b

Page 66

Students' responses will vary.

Page 67

Students' responses will vary.

Page 71

A. 5
3
2
4
1
8
7
6

B. Students' responses will vary.

Page 72

1. whinnied	5. reins
2. tidy	6. buggy
3. grazed	7. crockery
4. faint	8. prayer

Page 73

Students' responses will vary.

Page 74

1. triangles 36
diamonds 8

2. Colored quilts will vary.

3. Answers will vary.

Page 76

T
F
F
T
T
F
T

Answers to the second activity will vary.

Page 77

A. 1. activities   3. yarmulke
2. Sabbath   4. religion

B. Drawings will vary.

Page 78

A. "Jewish Jordan"

B. & C. Responses and drawings will vary.

Page 79

Bonus: slam dunk

Page 82

1. Louisiana

2. Fat Tuesday

3. a Cajun stew

4. The young men dress in colorful costumes and ride their horses through the countryside. They ask for gifts of food, which are made into a gumbo. People gather to eat gumbo, play music, and dance.

5. Answers will vary.

6. Students' responses will vary.

Page 83

shrimp   peppers
sing   tomatoes
celery   onion

Page 84

Students' drawings will vary.

Page 85

A. Possible responses include:
pot—not, hot, thought, brought, spot, taught, etc.
play—tray, say, delay, Mandalay, etc.
cook—took, book, crook, nook, etc.
fun—sun, begun, run, ton, etc.
B. Students' responses will vary.

Page 89

1. Mollee didn't like wearing it because it didn't look real. It also made her arm hurt and it was heavy. She wanted people to accept her the way she was.

2. Mollee couldn't believe the kids were so nice at her new school. She kept waiting for this to change. She was fearful that the kids might start mistreating her.

3. Mollee was excited about her new school, but she was also afraid of how the kids would react to her arm.

4. Answers will vary. Mollee and Jenaya both wish they could change something about themselves. They're different in the way they look and feel.

5. Answers will vary. The kids seem more accepting and mature to Mollee because they don't seem afraid of her disability. They ask her about it. They don't make fun of her.

Page 90

prosthesis
despised
satisfied
confident
cruel
optimistic
petite
inquired
casually

Page 91

1. 1, 2, 3	6. 1
2. 1	7. 1
3. 1	8. 1, 2
4. 1	9. 1
5. 1, 3	

Page 92
Students' responses will vary.

Page 96
1. He studied hard to get into a high school with a good baseball team; he practiced hard to improve his pitching skills.

2. Answers will vary, but may include the idea that Hideo was different because he was large and he was very talented at baseball. He was the same in that he had to go to school and take tests; he played in Little League.

3. His nickname is "Tornado" because of his whirling wind-up when he pitches.

4. He had an interpreter.

5. He wanted to play baseball in America.

Page 97
1. barrier
2. respectably
3. professional
4. achieve
5. dedication
6. interpreter
7. compete

Page 98
Students' responses will vary.

Page 99
Students' responses will vary.

Page 103
1. She had a stroke.

2. speaking, picking up a spoon, lifting a leg, holding a ball, wiggling her toes

3. She was frightened about what the kids would think and say when they saw her disability.

4. Answers will vary. Possible answers include *determined, courageous.* Examples should support the choice of word.

5. to count on being able to do with no difficulty

6. Answers will vary.

Page 104
1. regular
2. routine
3. love
4. drooped
5. worried
6. relaxed
7. intent on
8. luckily

Page 105
Determined—to play soccer again
Anxious—didn't want to start school wondered what all her classmates might say
Proud—that she became a stronger person because of her experience that she made the high school junior varsity soccer team
Athletic—made the high school junior varsity soccer team
Hardworking—she worked even harder at all her therapies she exercised an extra hour kicking the ball and running
Disappointed—that she didn't make the team her first tryout

Page 106
1. encyclopedia

2. *N* for nervous system because the brain is part of the nervous system.

3. F
   T
   T
   T
   F

Page 110
1. Answers will vary, but could include something about how hard it is to hide something about yourself; you feel as if you're lying.

2. Ben thinks his family adopted a white name to fit in. It possibly came from one of his family's employers.

3. Ben was first inspired to learn martial arts from Japanese American children. They worked with Ben in the fields. Although they were small, they were able to defend themselves by using judo.

4. Answers will vary, but could include the fact that Ben never gave up. He faced each new challenge that came his way. By doing this he was able to handle each problem with ease.

5. Answers will vary, but should address the idea that he stands up for what he believes is important, even if that is not popular.

Page 111
1. recognized
2. heritage
3. negative
4. cruel
5. discrimination
6. minorities
7. athletic
8. preferred

Clue: Native American

Page 112
Students' responses will vary.

Page 113
Possible responses include:
jewelry designer—creates beautiful jewelry, creativity, skill with tools
field worker—strength, willingness to work hard, good with hands and tools
U.S. senator—knowledge of government, ability to speak to people, able to remember lots of facts and infomation, tries to help the people he or she represents

Page 115
1. Dr. Maulana Karenga

2. 1966

3. Answers will vary.

4. A candle is lit each night to represent the seven principles of Kwanzaa.

5. Answers will vary.

6. It means "Hello, friends."

Page 116
A. 1. ancestors
   2. future
   3. pride
   4. heritage
   5. descent
   6. principles
   7. accomplishments
   8. faith
B. originated

Page 117
Students' responses will vary.

Page 118
1. flag   2, 5
2. map   4, 4
3. fruit   3, 2
4. drum   8, 4
5. corn   5, 3
6. candles   7, 6

Students' responses will vary.

Page 121

1. brave

2. T; He played four sports in high school and won awards in all those sports in college. He was the first to do this. As a professional baseball player, he won Rookie of the Year and Most Valuable Player awards. He was voted into baseball's Hall of Fame.

3. To "stick it out" means to stay with something even though it is difficult.

4. Answers will vary. Students may name his mother, a coach, or Branch Rickey. Accept answers that are supported by good reasoning.

5. Answers will vary.

Page 122

5
3
4
1
6
2

1. **pre**season
2. hope**ful**
3. **un**equal
4. **pre**dict
5. **un**fair
6. wonder**ful**
7. **un**happy

Page 123

Students' responses will vary.

Page 124

1. 40
2. Thursday and Saturday
3. 30
4. Answers will vary.

Page 127

1. southern California

2. She took gymnastics; students may conclude that gymnastics helped her learn body control and how to do complicated movements. Gymnastics also builds strength.

3. She decided to become a skater when she watched Brian Boitano win an Olympic gold medal in figure skating for the U.S.

4. Answers will vary, but may include: she feels as if she is flying; she feels at home; she feels that she is where she belongs, etc.

5. She skated all day long, seven days a week; even after disappointments, she kept skating; she gave up other activities to practice skating.

6. She won the reward of constant practice—the U.S. National Championships.

Page 128

A.
1. at ease
2. test
3. drill
4. persistence
5. winner
6. perfectly
7. undertake
8. contest

B. Answers will vary.

Page 129

Gymnastics—on mats or special equipment; most events do not use music

Ice-Skating—on ice skates; done to music

Both—need to be strong, coordinated; jumps, graceful moves; men and women participate; hard to learn; special clothing and equipment

Page 130

1. track
2. ice-skating
3. skiing
4. gymnastics
5. swimming
6. long jump

Page 134

1. As punishment for talking in class, he was sent to the school basement to read the Constitution.

2. He studied the words that said "all citizens have equal rights."

3. Marshall was bothered about segregation—that black Americans did not have equal rights. Examples include: not being able to buy houses in white neighborhoods, not being allowed to eat in certain restaurants or drink at "white" drinking fountains, not being allowed to attend the same schools as white students.

4. The Court decided that segregated schools were unequal.

5. Answers will vary.

Page 135

A.
1. equal
2. argue
3. segregate
4. appointed
5. appreciate
6. potential
7. memorize
8. achievement

B. dedicated

Page 136

Students' drawings and responses will vary.

Page 137

1909—Marshall was born.

1925—Marshall started college at Lincoln University in Pennsylvania.

1929—Marshall began law school at Howard University.

1933—Marshall began practicing law.

1953—Marshall took the case Brown v. the Board of Education to the U.S. Supreme Court.

1967—President Johnson appointed Marshall to the Supreme Court.

1991—Marshall resigned from the Supreme Court.

1993—Marshall died.

Page 139

Students' drawings and responses will vary.